KT-104-658

Intermediate 2 | Units 1, 2 & 3

Mathematics

"2000" Specimen Question Paper
Paper 1 (Non-calculator)
Paper 2

Additional Specimen Question Paper
Paper 1 (Non-calculator)
Paper 2

2001
Paper 1 (Non-calculator)
Paper 2

2002
Paper 1 (Non-calculator)
Paper 2

2002 Winter Diet
Paper 1 (Non-calculator)
Paper 2

2003 Exam
Paper 1 (Non-calculator)
Paper 2

First exam published in 2000.
Published by
Leckie & Leckie, 8 Whitehill Terrace, St. Andrews, Scotland KY16 8RN
tel: 01334 475656 fax: 01334 477392
enquiries@leckieandleckie.co.uk www.leckieandleckie.co.uk

Leckie & Leckie Project Team: Peter Dennis; John MacPherson; Bruce Ryan; Andrea Smith

ISBN 1-84372-115-5

A CIP Catalogue record for this book is available from the British Library.

Printed in Scotland by Scotprint.

Leckie & Leckie is a division of Granada Learning Limited, part of Granada plc.

Leckie & Leckie
Scotland's leading educational publishers

Introduction

Dear Student,

This past paper book provides you with the perfect opportunity to put into practice everything you need to know in order to excel in your exams. The range of past papers offers you an invaluable insight into what to expect on the day and will help you to prepare thoroughly for your own exam this summer.

Work carefully through each past paper: the questions are designed to assess not only your subject knowledge and understanding, but also your ability to apply examinable skills developed throughout your course. By referring to the answer booklet at the back of the book you will understand exactly what the examiner is looking for to gain a top mark and will be able to focus on and improve in particular areas of your course which you find difficult. Remember too to use the top tips for revision and sitting the exam to make sure you perform to the best of your ability.

Practice makes perfect. Use these past papers to make sure you know what to expect on the day and are ready to succeed.

Good luck!

Acknowledgements

Every effort has been made to trace the copyright holders and to obtain their permission for the use of copyright material. Leckie & Leckie will gladly receive information enabling them to rectify any error or omission in subsequent editions.

INTERMEDIATE 2 2000 SQP

[CO56/SQP201]

NATIONAL
QUALIFICATIONS

Time: 45 minutes

Specimen Question Paper
(based on the 2000 Question Paper)

MATHEMATICS
INTERMEDIATE 2
Units 1, 2 and 3
Paper 1
(Non-calculator)

Read carefully

1 **You may NOT use a calculator.**
2 Full credit will be given only where the solution contains appropriate working.
3 Square-ruled paper is provided.

SCOTTISH
QUALIFICATIONS
AUTHORITY

FORMULAE LIST

The roots of $ax^2 + bx + c = 0$ are $x = \dfrac{-b \pm \sqrt{(b^2 - 4ac)}}{2a}$

Sine rule: $\dfrac{a}{\sin A} = \dfrac{b}{\sin B} = \dfrac{c}{\sin C}$

Cosine rule: $a^2 = b^2 + c^2 - 2bc \cos A$ or $\cos A = \dfrac{b^2 + c^2 - a^2}{2bc}$

Area of a triangle: Area $= \frac{1}{2}ab \sin C$

Volume of a sphere: Volume $= \dfrac{4}{3}\pi r^3$

Volume of a cone: Volume $= \dfrac{1}{3}\pi r^2 h$

Volume of a cylinder: Volume $= \pi r^2 h$

Standard deviation: $s = \sqrt{\dfrac{\Sigma(x - \bar{x})^2}{n - 1}} = \sqrt{\dfrac{\Sigma x^2 - (\Sigma x)^2 / n}{n - 1}}$, where n is the sample size.

Marks

1. A group of students scored the following marks in a test.

9 5 6 8 6 9 7 8 6 5

(*a*) Construct a frequency table from the above data and add a cumulative frequency column. **2**

(*b*) What is the probability that a student chosen at random from this group scored less than 8? **1**

2.

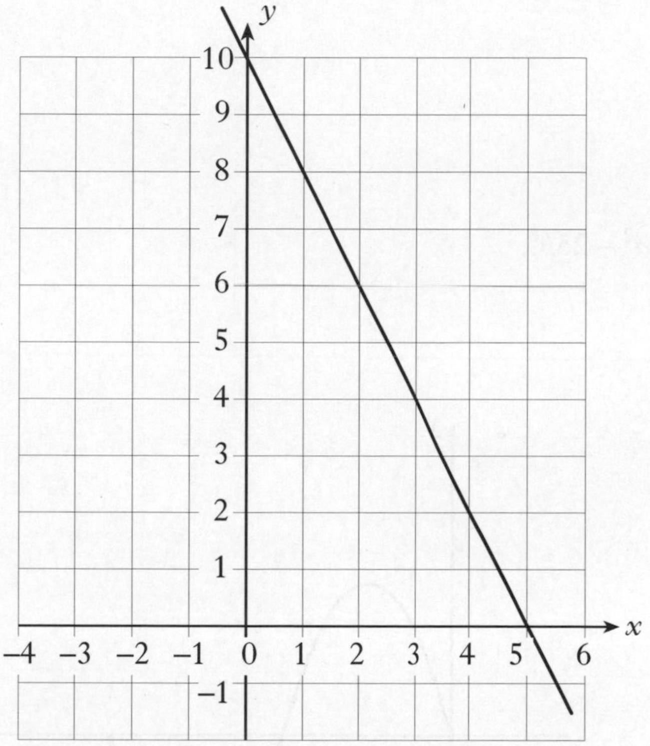

Find the equation of the straight line. **3**

[Turn over

Marks

3. The diagram below shows the graph of $y = ax^2$.

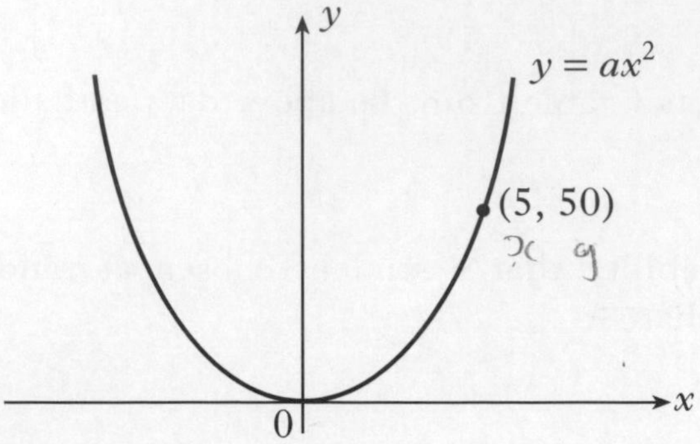

Find the value of a. **2**

4. Factorise

$$9a^2 - 25b^2.$$ **2**

5.

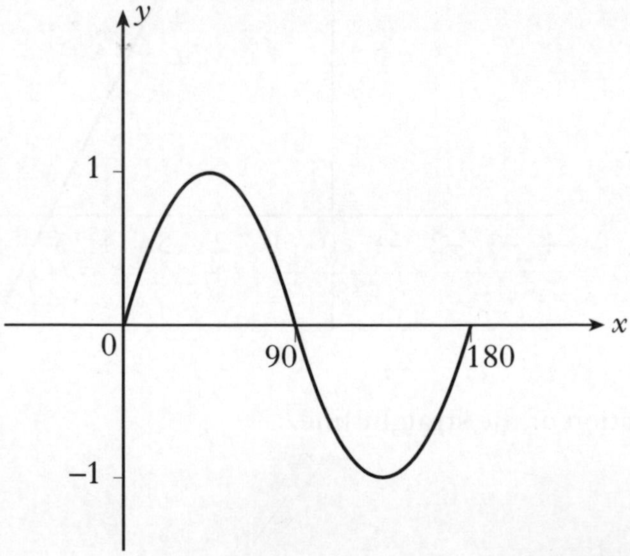

The graph of $y = \sin bx°$ is shown in the diagram.

State the value of b. **1**

Marks

6. (*a*) Express $\dfrac{a^{\frac{1}{2}} \times a^{\frac{5}{2}}}{a^2}$ in its simplest form. **2**

(*b*) Express $\dfrac{2}{\sqrt{3}}$ as a fraction with a rational denominator. **2**

(*c*) Express $\dfrac{2}{x} + \dfrac{4}{x+3}$, $x \neq 0$, $x \neq -3$, as a single fraction in its simplest form. **3**

7.

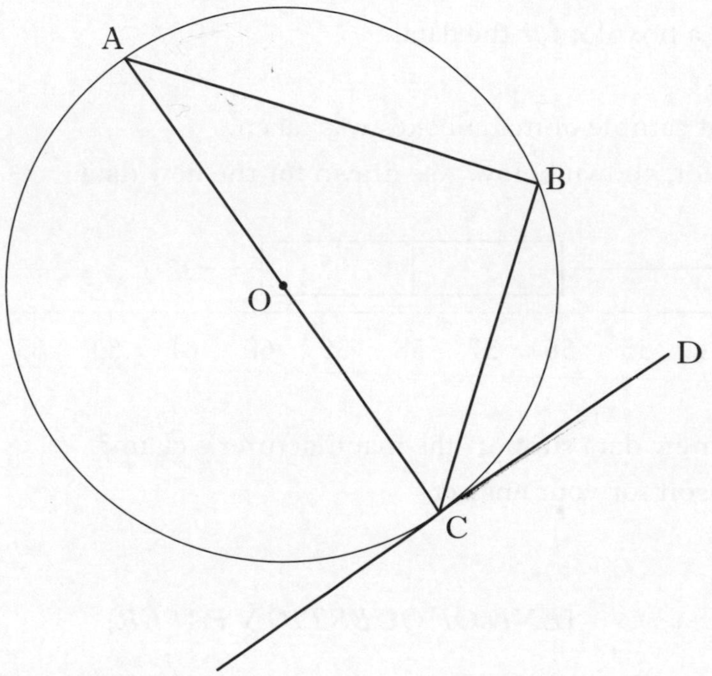

- A, B and C are points on the circumference of a circle, centre O.
- CD is a tangent to the circle.
- Angle BCD = 25 °.

Calculate the size of angle BAC.

Show all working. **3**

[Turn over for Question 8 on *Page six*

Marks

8. A manufacturer of matches claims that there are "on average 60 matches per box".

A sample of eleven boxes contains the following numbers of matches per box.

58, 62, 60, 65, 59, 60, 59, 62, 61, 61, 64

(*a*) From the above data, find the median, the lower quartile and the upper quartile. **2**

(*b*) Comment on the claim made above. **1**

(*c*) Construct a boxplot for the data. **2**

(*d*) A different sample of matchboxes was taken.

The boxplot, shown below, was drawn for the new data.

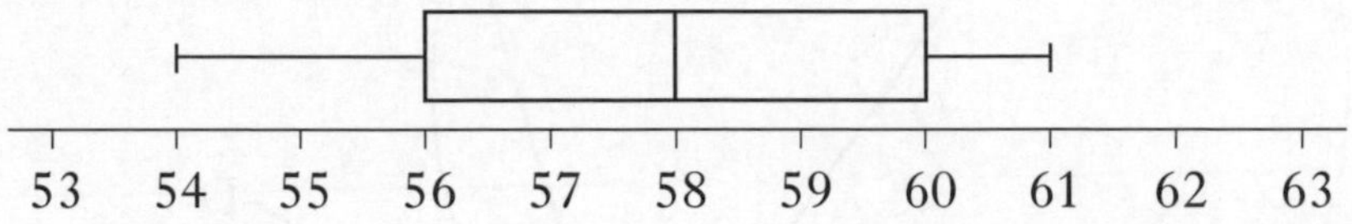

Does this new data support the manufacturer's claim?

Give a reason for your answer. **1**

[*END OF QUESTION PAPER*]

[CO56/SQP201]

NATIONAL QUALIFICATIONS

Time: 1 hour 30 minutes

MATHEMATICS
INTERMEDIATE 2
Units 1, 2 and 3
Paper 2

Specimen Question Paper
(based on the 2000 Question Paper)

Read carefully

1 **Calculators may be used in this paper.**

2 Full credit will be given only where the solution contains appropriate working.

3 Square-ruled paper is provided.

SCOTTISH QUALIFICATIONS AUTHORITY

FORMULAE LIST

The roots of $ax^2 + bx + c = 0$ are $x = \dfrac{-b \pm \sqrt{(b^2 - 4ac)}}{2a}$

Sine rule: $\dfrac{a}{\sin A} = \dfrac{b}{\sin B} = \dfrac{c}{\sin C}$

Cosine rule: $a^2 = b^2 + c^2 - 2bc \cos A$ or $\cos A = \dfrac{b^2 + c^2 - a^2}{2bc}$

Area of a triangle: Area $= \frac{1}{2}ab \sin C$

Volume of a sphere: Volume $= \frac{4}{3}\pi r^3$

Volume of a cone: Volume $= \frac{1}{3}\pi r^2 h$

Volume of a cylinder: Volume $= \pi r^2 h$

Standard deviation: $s = \sqrt{\dfrac{\Sigma(x - \bar{x})^2}{n - 1}} = \sqrt{\dfrac{\Sigma x^2 - (\Sigma x)^2 / n}{n - 1}}$, where n is the sample size.

Marks

1. A hotel inspector recorded the volume of wine, in millilitres, in a sample of six glasses.

120 126 125 131 130 124

Use an appropriate formula to calculate the standard deviation.
Show clearly all your working. **4**

2. Multiply out the brackets and collect like terms.

$$(3x + 2)(x - 1) + 4x$$ **3**

3. The diagram shows a fold-away table whose top is in the shape of part of a circle.

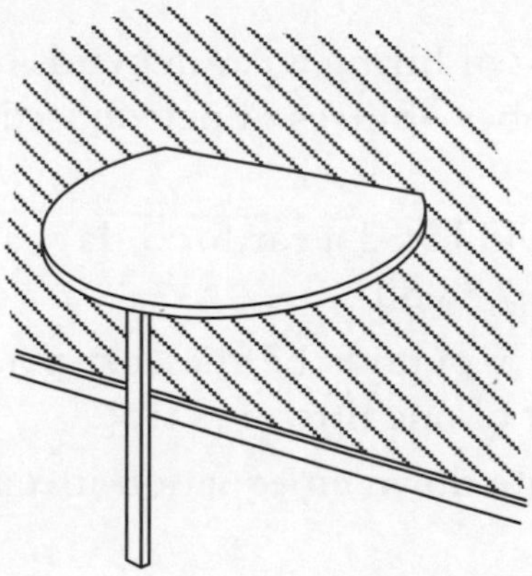

- The centre of the circle is O.
- AB is a chord of the circle.
- AB is 70 centimetres.
- The radius, OA, is 40 centimetres.

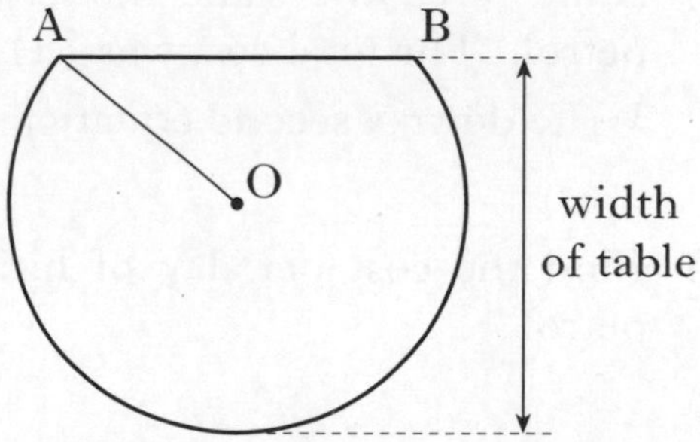

Find the width of the table. **4**

[Turn over

Marks

4. Michael wishes to borrow £1000 for 3 months. He can choose from **Advantage Loans** or **Low Cost Loans**.

Advantage Loans

INTEREST RATE

1·5% per month

Low Cost Loans

INTEREST RATE

18·5% per annum

Which company costs less?
Give a reason for your answer. **4**

5. The cost of hiring a car depends on the number of days the car is hired and the number of litres of petrol used.

(*a*) David hired a car for 3 days and used 50 litres of petrol. The total cost was £88·50.
Let x pounds be the cost per day of hiring a car, and y pounds be the cost of one litre of petrol.
Write down an equation in x and y which satisfies the above condition. **1**

(*b*) Anne hired the same model of car for 4 days and used 60 litres of petrol. The total cost was £113·00.
Write down a second equation in x and y which satisfies this condition. **1**

(*c*) Find the cost per day of hiring the car and the cost of one litre of petrol. **4**

Marks

6. (*a*) Change the subject of the formula $r = \dfrac{st}{q}$ to s. **2**

(*b*) Use an appropriate formula to solve the quadratic equation

$$3x^2 - 2x - 6 = 0.$$

Give your answer correct to 1 decimal place. **4**

7. A bread bin is in the shape of a prism as shown below.

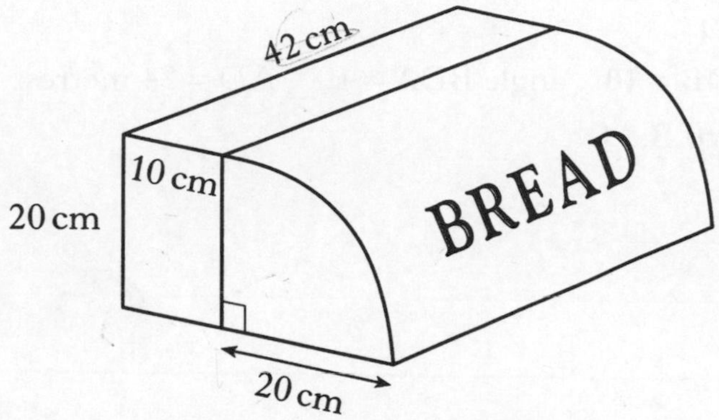

The cross-section of the bread bin consists of a rectangle 20 centimetres by 10 centimetres and a quarter circle.

(*a*) Calculate the volume of the bread bin.
Give your answer in cubic centimetres, correct to 3 significant figures. **4**

(*b*) The design is changed so that the volume remains the same. The cross-section is now a rectangle 20 centimetres by 10 centimetres and a right-angled triangle as shown in the diagram below.

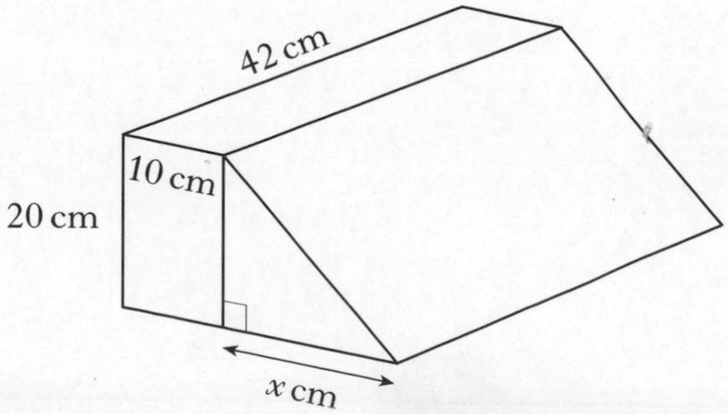

Find x. **3**

[Turn over

Marks

8.

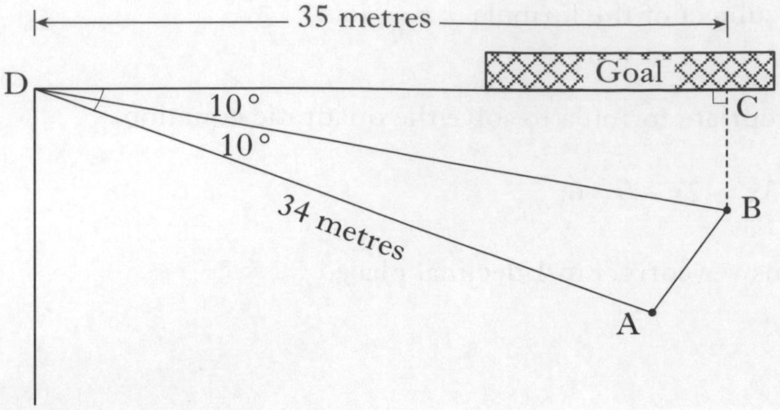

The diagram shows part of a football pitch with players at A, B, C and D.

BC is perpendicular to CD.

CD = 35 metres, angle CDB = 10 °, angle BDA = 10 °, AD = 34 metres.

Find the distance from A to B. **5**

Marks

9.

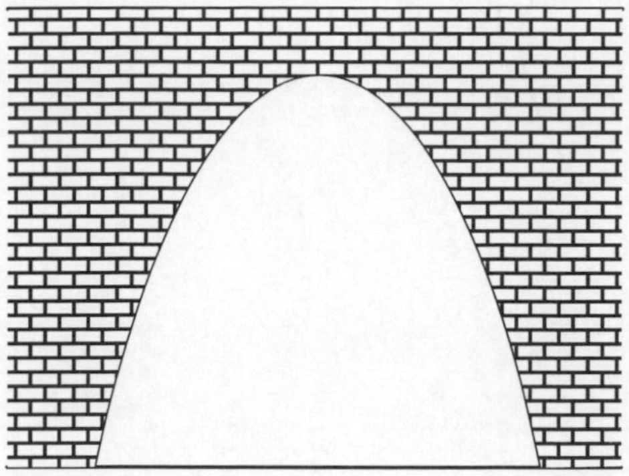

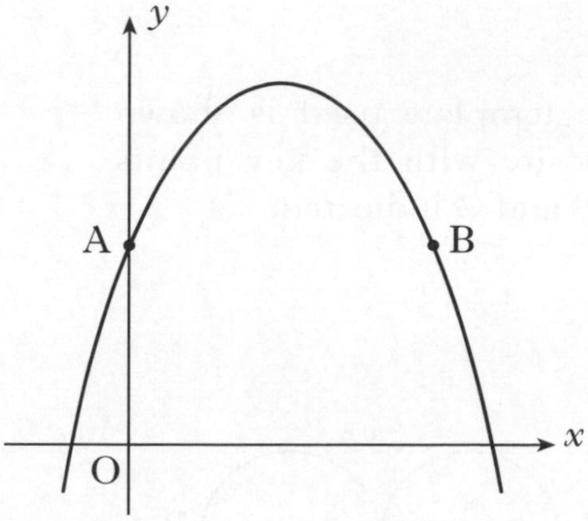

The arch of a railway bridge is represented by a parabola. The equation of the parabola is

$$y = 20 - (x - 3)^2.$$

(*a*) State the coordinates of the maximum turning point of the parabola. **2**

(*b*) State the equation of the axis of symmetry. **1**

(*c*) Points A and B have the same *y*-coordinate.
A is the point (0, 11). State the coordinates of B. **2**

10. (*a*) Solve the equation

$$4\sin x° - 1 = 0, \qquad 0 \le x < 360.$$ **3**

(*b*) Show that

$$\frac{1-\cos^2 A}{\cos^2 A} = \tan^2 A.$$ **2**

[Turn over for Question 11 on *Page eight*

Marks

11. Heart-shaped cards have been designed for St Valentine's Day.

The template used is shown opposite with the key points A, B and C indicated.

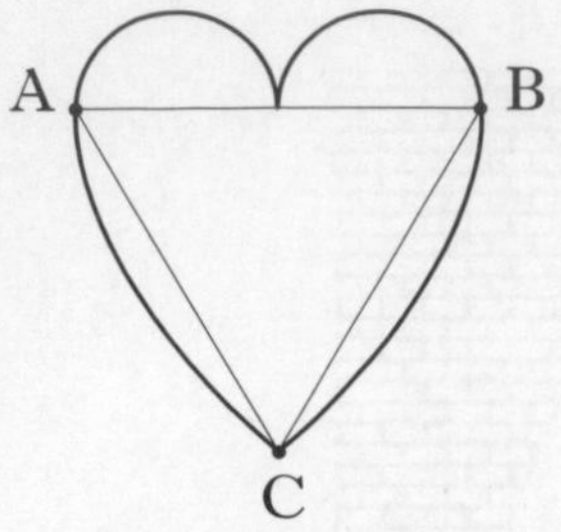

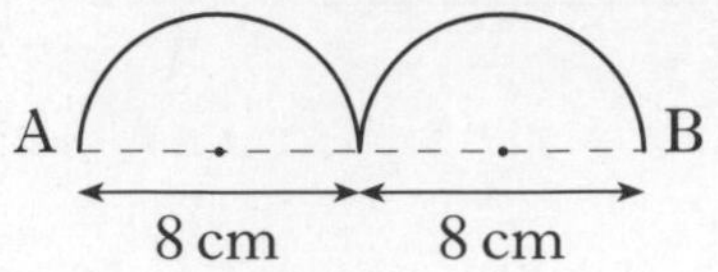

The top of the template was formed by drawing two semi-circles, each with diameter 8 centimetres.

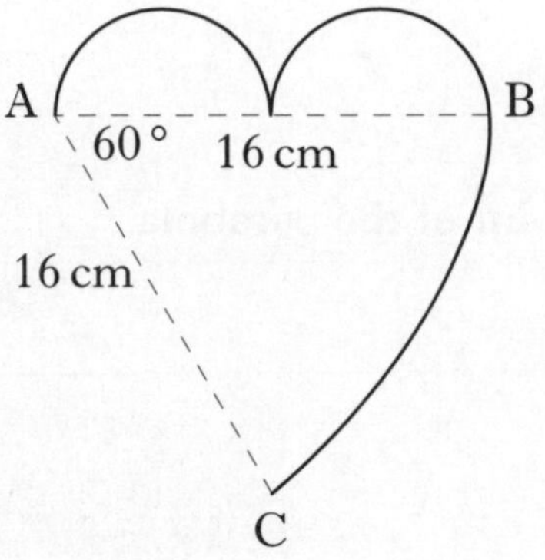

One side of the template was formed by drawing an arc BC of a circle centre A, where angle BAC = 60 °.

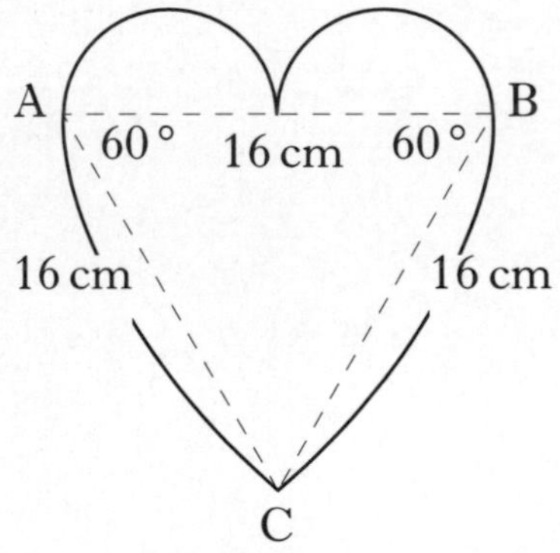

The template was completed by drawing arc AC of a circle centre B, where angle ABC = 60 °.

Find the perimeter of the template. **5**

[*END OF QUESTION PAPER*]

INTERMEDIATE 2
ADDITIONAL SQP

X100/201

NATIONAL QUALIFICATIONS

Time: 35 minutes

MATHEMATICS INTERMEDIATE 2

Units 1, 2 and 3

Paper 1

(Non-calculator)

ADDITIONAL SPECIMEN QUESTION PAPER

Read carefully

1 **You may NOT use a calculator.**

2 Full credit will be given only where the solution contains appropriate working.

3 Square-ruled paper is provided.

FORMULAE LIST

The roots of $ax^2 + bx + c = 0$ are $x = \dfrac{-b \pm \sqrt{(b^2 - 4ac)}}{2a}$

Sine rule: $\dfrac{a}{\sin A} = \dfrac{b}{\sin B} = \dfrac{c}{\sin C}$

Cosine rule: $a^2 = b^2 + c^2 - 2bc \cos A$ or $\cos A = \dfrac{b^2 + c^2 - a^2}{2bc}$

Area of a triangle: $\text{Area} = \frac{1}{2}ab \sin C$

Volume of a sphere: $\text{Volume} = \frac{4}{3}\pi r^3$

Volume of a cone: $\text{Volume} = \frac{1}{3}\pi r^2 h$

Volume of a cylinder: $\text{Volume} = \pi r^2 h$

Standard deviation: $s = \sqrt{\dfrac{\Sigma(x - \bar{x})^2}{n-1}} = \sqrt{\dfrac{\Sigma x^2 - (\Sigma x)^2/n}{n-1}}$, where n is the sample size.

ALL questions should be attempted.

Marks

1.

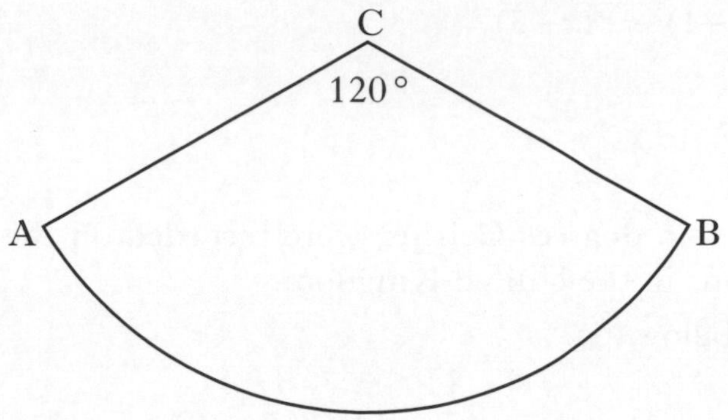

The diagram shows a sector of a circle, centre C and radius 15 centimetres.

AC and BC are radii.

Angle ACB is 120°.

Calculate the length of the arc AB.

(Take $\pi = 3{\cdot}14$) **3**

2.

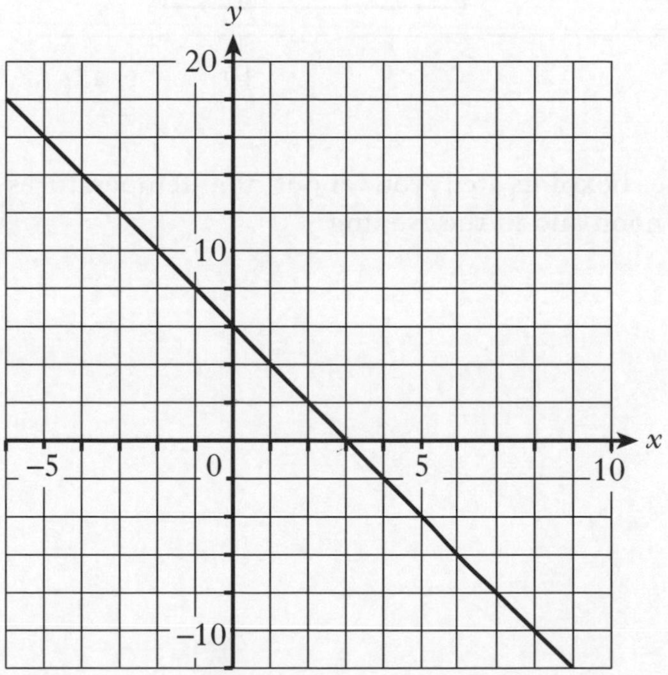

Find the equation of the straight line shown in the diagram. **3**

[Turn over

Marks

3. Multiply out the brackets and collect like terms.

$$5x(2x-1) - x(x-3)$$ **3**

4. The noon temperatures, in degrees Celsius, were recorded on the first day of June across the regions in the United Kingdom.

The results are shown below.

14	13	16	16	16	15	14	15	14
16	17	16	17	18	16	15	19	

(*a*) From the results, find the median, the lower quartile and the upper quartile. **3**

(*b*) Construct a boxplot for the data. **2**

(*c*) On the evening of the same day, the temperatures were again recorded.

The boxplot below was drawn for this data.

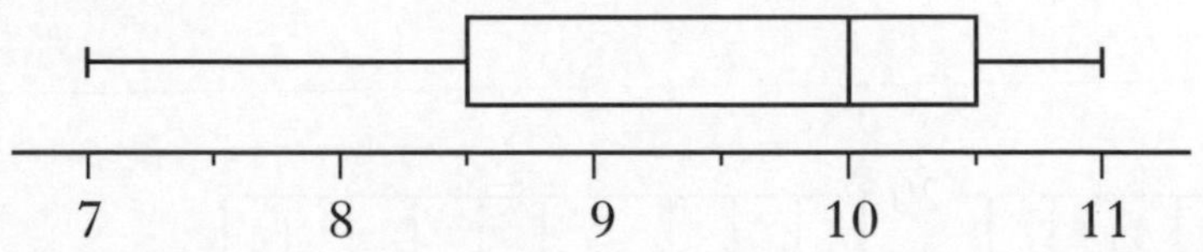

What do the boxplots tell you about the temperatures and their variability at noon and in the evening? **2**

Marks

5. The diagram below shows the graph of $y = (x + a)^2 + b$.

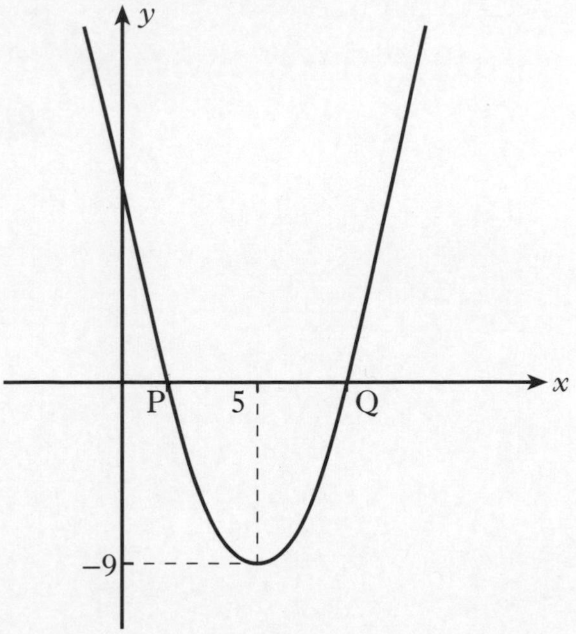

(*a*) Find the values of *a* and *b*. **2**

(*b*) State the equation of the axis of symmetry. **1**

(*c*) Find the coordinates of P and Q. **3**

6. Express $\frac{5}{\sqrt{3}}$ as a fraction with a rational denominator. **2**

7. Prove that

$$\tan x^\circ \cos x^\circ = \sin x^\circ.$$ **2**

[*END OF QUESTION PAPER*]

[BLANK PAGE]

X100/203

NATIONAL QUALIFICATIONS

Time: 35 minutes

MATHEMATICS
INTERMEDIATE 2
Units 1, 2 and 3
Paper 2

ADDITIONAL SPECIMEN QUESTION PAPER

Read carefully

1. **Calculators may be used in this paper.**
2. Full credit will be given only where the solution contains appropriate working.
3. Square-ruled paper is provided.

SCOTTISH QUALIFICATIONS AUTHORITY

FORMULAE LIST

The roots of $ax^2 + bx + c = 0$ are $x = \dfrac{-b \pm \sqrt{(b^2 - 4ac)}}{2a}$

Sine rule: $\dfrac{a}{\sin A} = \dfrac{b}{\sin B} = \dfrac{c}{\sin C}$

Cosine rule: $a^2 = b^2 + c^2 - 2bc \cos A$ or $\cos A = \dfrac{b^2 + c^2 - a^2}{2bc}$

Area of a triangle: Area $= \frac{1}{2}ab \sin C$

Volume of a sphere: Volume $= \frac{4}{3}\pi r^3$

Volume of a cone: Volume $= \frac{1}{3}\pi r^2 h$

Volume of a cylinder: Volume $= \pi r^2 h$

Standard deviation: $s = \sqrt{\dfrac{\Sigma(x - \bar{x})^2}{n-1}} = \sqrt{\dfrac{\Sigma x^2 - (\Sigma x)^2 / n}{n-1}}$, where n is the sample size.

ALL questions should be attempted.

Marks

1. One hundred milligrams of an antibiotic are given to a patient.

   At the end of each hour the number of milligrams of antibiotic in the body is 20% less than at the beginning of that hour.

   How many milligrams of antibiotic remain in the body at the end of three hours? **3**

2. 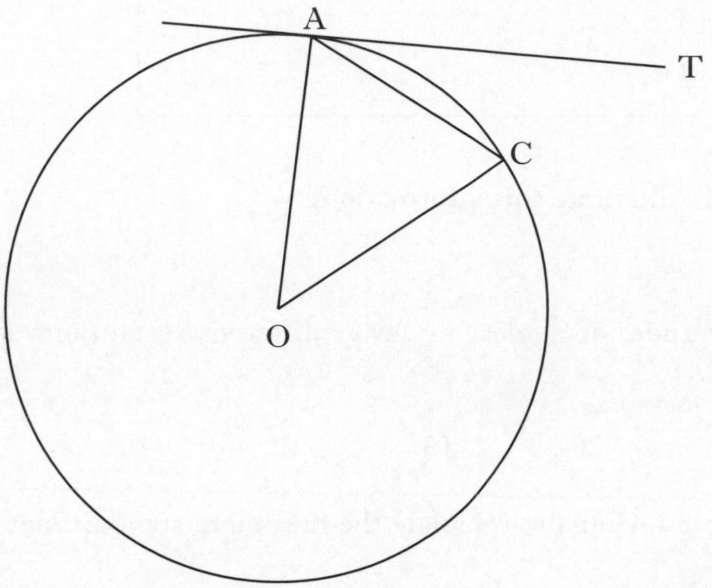

   AT is a tangent to the circle, centre O.

   Angle TAC is 26 °.

   Calculate the size of angle AOC. **3**

3. Solve **algebraically** the system of equations

$$5x + 3y = 1$$
$$3x - 2y = 12.$$

3

[Turn over

Marks

4. A tutor asked students in his year group where they planned to go on holiday.

The responses are shown below.

Holiday	Frequency
UK	26
Europe (not UK)	63
USA	16
Others	15

Draw a piechart to illustrate this information. **4**

5. The price, in pounds, of a meal in seven different restaurants is shown below.

17 11 20 13 12 10 15

Use an appropriate formula to calculate the mean and standard deviation of these prices.

Show clearly all your working. **4**

6. A triangular plot of ground, PRQ, is represented below.

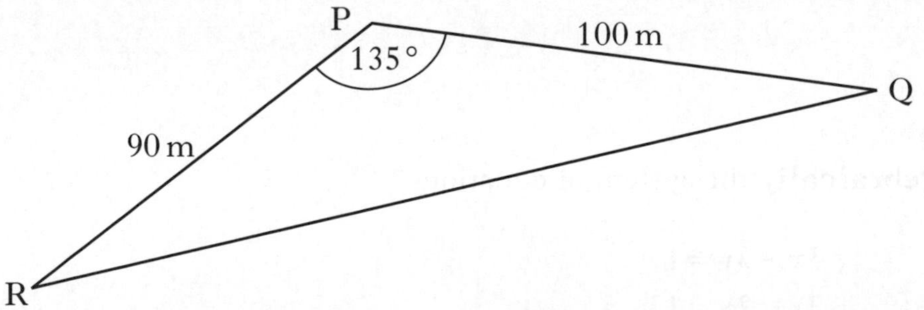

PQ = 100 metres, PR = 90 metres and angle RPQ = 135 °.

Calculate the length of RQ.

Do not use a scale drawing. **4**

Marks

7. (*a*) Factorise

$$2x^2 + 5x - 3.$$ **2**

(*b*) Hence express

$$\frac{2x^2 + 5x - 3}{4x - 2}$$

in its simplest form. **3**

8. (*a*)

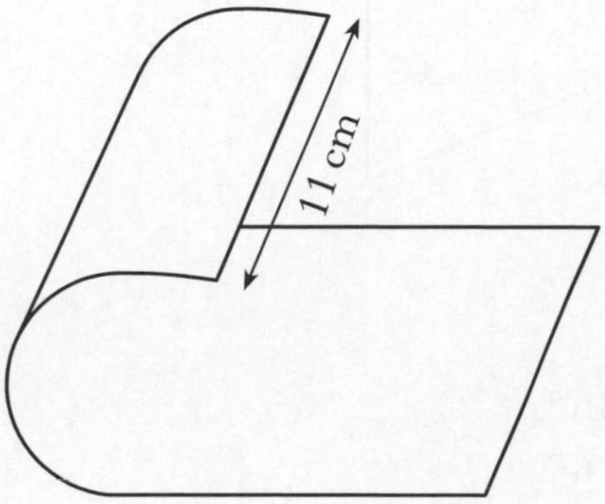

A strip of metal, 11 centimetres wide, is rolled into the cylindrical wall of a can.

The radius of the base of the can is 4 centimetres.

Calculate the volume of the cylindrical can.

Give your answer correct to two significant figures. **3**

(*b*) Another cylindrical can which has a volume of 500 cubic centimetres is constructed using a strip of metal 15 centimetres wide.

Calculate the base radius of this can. **3**

9. Solve the equation

$$2x^2 - 4x - 5 = 0$$

giving your answers correct to one decimal place. **4**

[Turn over

Marks

10. The diagram below shows the position of three towns E, B and F.

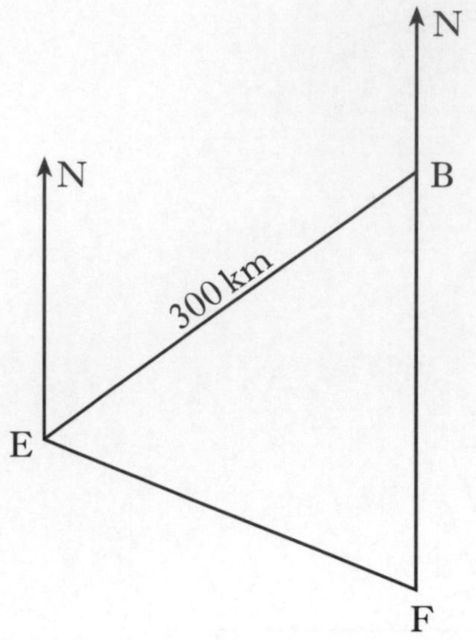

B is 300 kilometres from E.

From E, the bearing of B is 046 °.

From E, the bearing of F is 116 °.

F is due south of B.

How far apart are the towns E and F? **5**

11. (*a*) Simplify

$$x^3\,(2 + x^{-3}).$$ **3**

(*b*) Change the subject of the formula

$$c = \frac{x^2 - d}{e}$$

to x. **3**

Marks

12. The diagram below shows a road bridge.

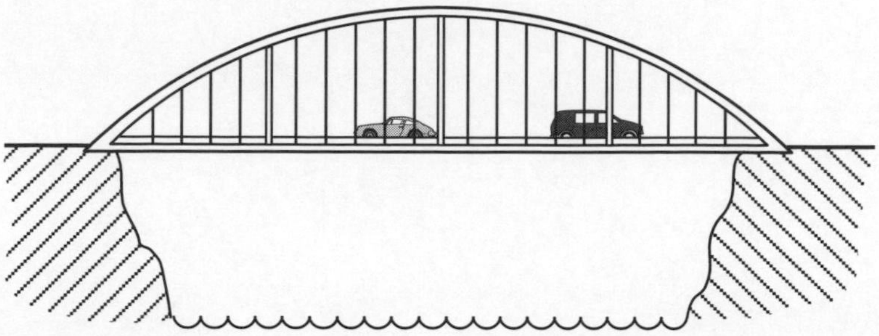

The curved part of the bridge is formed from an arc of a circle.

In the figure below,

- A represents the centre of the circle
- CD represents the horizontal distance between the ends of the bridge
- CD is 200 metres
- AC and AD are radii
- AC is 180 metres.

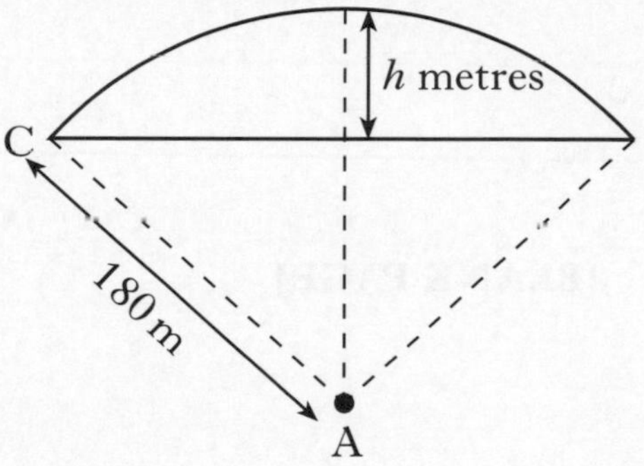

Find the height, h metres, of the bridge above its ends. **4**

13. Solve the equation

$$5\cos x^\circ + 3 = 0,\ 0 \leq x \leq 360.$$ **3**

[*END OF QUESTION PAPER*]

[BLANK PAGE]

INTERMEDIATE 2 2001

X056/201

NATIONAL
QUALIFICATIONS
2001

THURSDAY, 17 MAY
9.00 AM – 9.45 AM

MATHEMATICS
INTERMEDIATE 2
Units 1, 2 and 3
Paper 1
(Non-calculator)

Read carefully

1 **You may NOT use a calculator.**

2 Full credit will be given only where the solution contains appropriate working.

3 Square-ruled paper is provided.

SCOTTISH
QUALIFICATIONS
AUTHORITY

FORMULAE LIST

The roots of $ax^2 + bx + c = 0$ are $x = \dfrac{-b \pm \sqrt{(b^2 - 4ac)}}{2a}$

Sine rule: $\dfrac{a}{\sin A} = \dfrac{b}{\sin B} = \dfrac{c}{\sin C}$

Cosine rule: $a^2 = b^2 + c^2 - 2bc \cos A$ or $\cos A = \dfrac{b^2 + c^2 - a^2}{2bc}$

Area of a triangle: $\text{Area} = \frac{1}{2}ab \sin C$

Volume of a sphere: $\text{Volume} = \frac{4}{3}\pi r^3$

Volume of a cone: $\text{Volume} = \frac{1}{3}\pi r^2 h$

Volume of a cylinder: $\text{Volume} = \pi r^2 h$

Standard deviation: $s = \sqrt{\dfrac{\Sigma(x - \bar{x})^2}{n - 1}} = \sqrt{\dfrac{\Sigma x^2 - (\Sigma x)^2 / n}{n - 1}}$, where n is the sample size.

ALL questions should be attempted.

Marks

1. Factorise

$x^2 + 2x - 15.$ **2**

2.

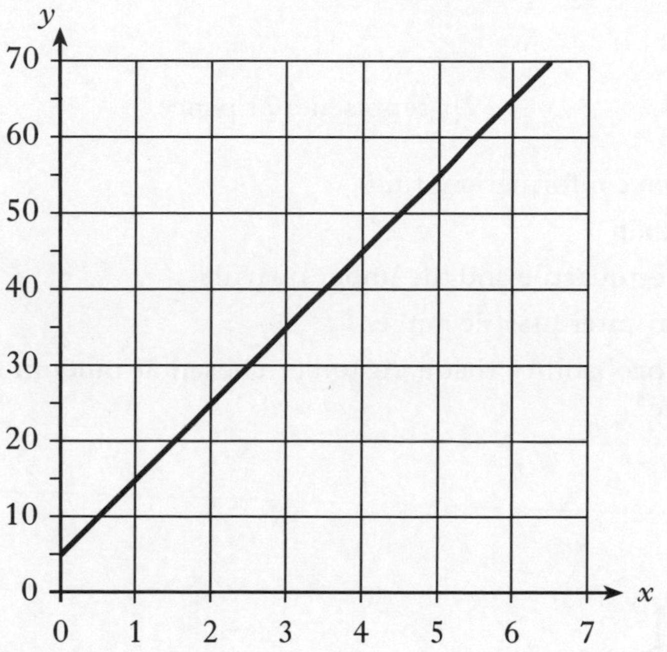

Find the equation of the straight line. **3**

3. Find the point of intersection of the straight lines with equations $2x + y = 5$ and $x - 3y = 6$. **4**

4. $P = R^2b - 5$

Change the subject of the formula to R. **3**

[Turn over

Marks

5. The stem and leaf diagram shows the amounts of money spent by customers in a shop.

2	1 4 4
3	0 1 5 5 8
4	1 2 3 5 6 9
5	0 1 2 3 5 8 9 9
6	0 0 1 2 6
7	1 2 2
8	0 4 6

$n = 33$ 2|1 represents 21 pence

(*a*) Using the above information, find

(i) the median **1**

(ii) the lower quartile and the upper quartile **2**

(iii) the semi-interquartile range. **2**

(*b*) What is the probability that a customer chosen at random spent more than 80 pence? **1**

6.

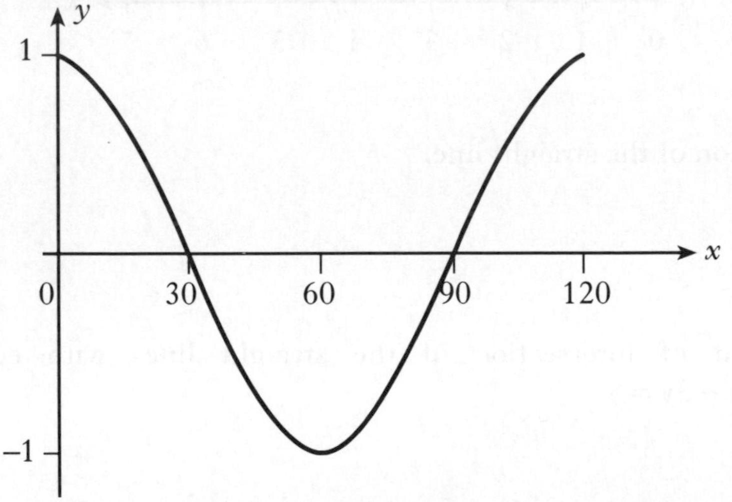

Part of the graph of $y = \cos bx°$ is shown in the diagram.

State the value of b. **1**

Marks

7. The square and rectangle shown below have the same **perimeter**.

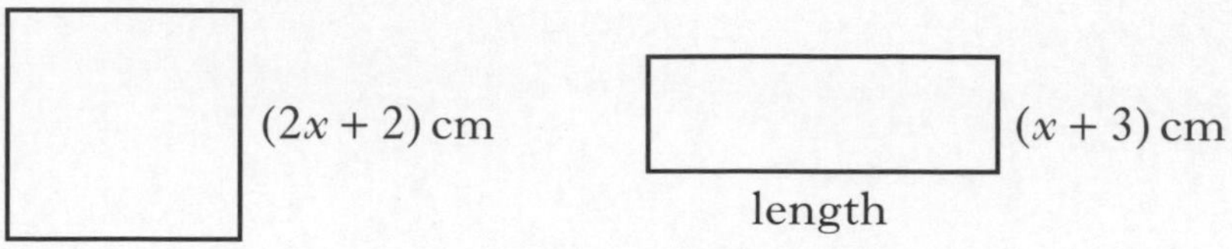

Show that the length of the rectangle is $(3x + 1)$ centimetres. **2**

8. (*a*) Express $\frac{3}{x} - \frac{5}{x+2}$, $x \neq 0$, $x \neq -2$, as a single fraction in its simplest form. **3**

(*b*) Express $\sqrt{18} - \sqrt{2} + \sqrt{72}$ as a surd in its simplest form. **3**

[*END OF QUESTION PAPER*]

[BLANK PAGE]

X056/203

NATIONAL
QUALIFICATIONS
2001

THURSDAY, 17 MAY
10.05 AM – 11.35 AM

MATHEMATICS
INTERMEDIATE 2
Units 1, 2 and 3
Paper 2

Read carefully

1 **Calculators may be used in this paper.**

2 Full credit will be given only where the solution contains appropriate working.

3 Square-ruled paper is provided.

SCOTTISH
QUALIFICATIONS
AUTHORITY

FORMULAE LIST

The roots of $ax^2 + bx + c = 0$ are $x = \dfrac{-b \pm \sqrt{(b^2 - 4ac)}}{2a}$

Sine rule: $\dfrac{a}{\sin A} = \dfrac{b}{\sin B} = \dfrac{c}{\sin C}$

Cosine rule: $a^2 = b^2 + c^2 - 2bc \cos A$ or $\cos A = \dfrac{b^2 + c^2 - a^2}{2bc}$

Area of a triangle: $\text{Area} = \frac{1}{2}ab \sin C$

Volume of a sphere: $\text{Volume} = \frac{4}{3}\pi r^3$

Volume of a cone: $\text{Volume} = \frac{1}{3}\pi r^2 h$

Volume of a cylinder: $\text{Volume} = \pi r^2 h$

Standard deviation: $s = \sqrt{\dfrac{\sum(x - \bar{x})^2}{n-1}} = \sqrt{\dfrac{\sum x^2 - (\sum x)^2 / n}{n-1}}$, where n is the sample size.

ALL questions should be attempted.

Marks

1. The population of a city is increasing at a steady rate of 2·4% per annum. The present population is 528 000.

   What is the expected population in 4 years time?

   Give your answer to the nearest thousand. **3**

2. Two groups of six students are given the same test.

   (*a*) The marks of Group A are

   73 47 59 71 48 62.

   Use an appropriate formula to calculate the mean and the standard deviation.

   Show clearly all your working. **4**

   (*b*) In Group B, the mean is 60 and the standard deviation is 29·8.

   Compare the results of the two groups. **2**

3. The contents of twenty matchboxes were counted.

44	44	46	45	47	48	47	41	48	45
45	44	42	43	44	46	46	43	49	45

   (*a*) Construct a dot plot for the data. **2**

   (*b*) Describe the shape of the distribution. **1**

   (*c*) What would you expect the "average contents per matchbox" to be ? **1**

[Turn over

Marks

4. Gordon and Brian leave a hostel at the same time.

Gordon walks on a bearing of 045 ° at a speed of 4·4 kilometres per hour.

Brian walks on a bearing of 100 ° at a speed of 4·8 kilometres per hour.

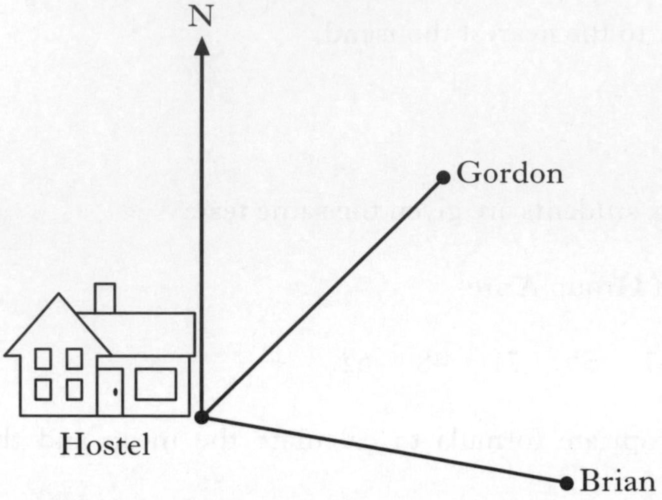

If they both walk at steady speeds, how far apart will they be after 2 hours? **5**

5.

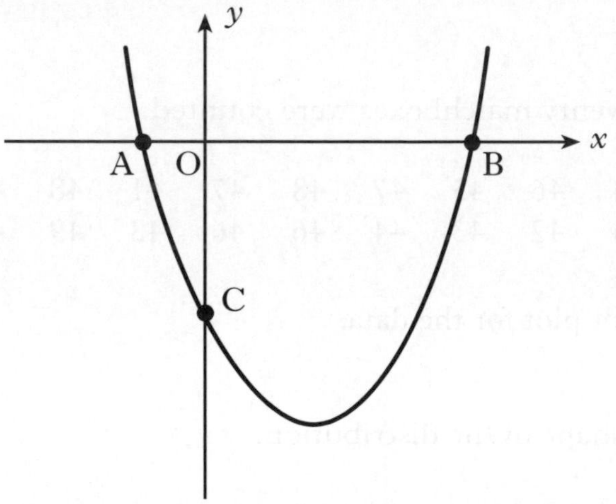

The equation of the parabola in the above diagram is

$$y = (x - 2)^2 - 9.$$

(*a*) State the coordinates of the minimum turning point of the parabola. **2**

(*b*) Find the coordinates of C. **2**

(*c*) A is the point (–1, 0). State the coordinates of B. **1**

Mark

6. A drinks container is in the shape of a cylinder with radius 20 centimetres and height 50 centimetres.

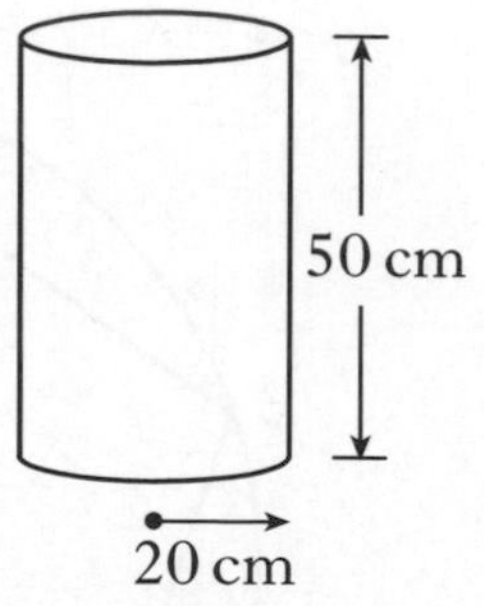

(*a*) Calculate the volume of the drinks container.

Give your answer in cubic centimetres, correct to two significant figures. **3**

(*b*) Liquid from the full container can fill 800 cups, in the shape of cones, each of radius 3 centimetres.

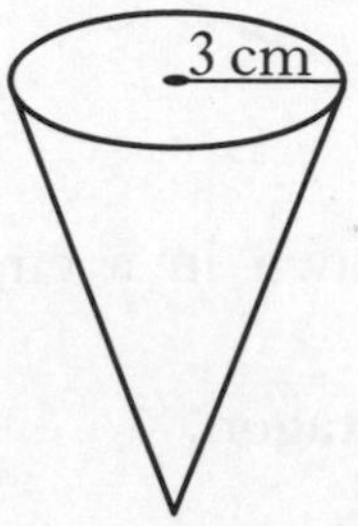

What will be the height of liquid in each cup? **4**

7. Multiply out the brackets and collect like terms.

$$(x + 4)(2x^2 + 3x - 1)$$ **3**

[Turn over

Marks

8.

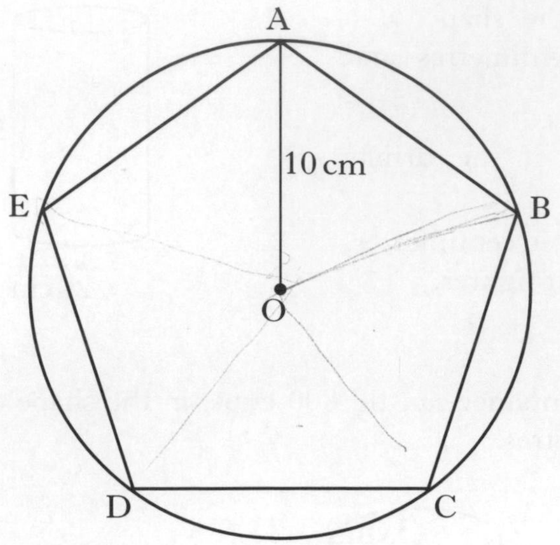

A regular pentagon ABCDE is drawn in a circle, centre O, with radius 10 centimetres.

Calculate the area of the regular pentagon. **5**

9. (*a*) Express $a^2(2a^{-\frac{1}{2}} + a)$ in its simplest form. **2**

(*b*) Solve the quadratic equation

$$3x^2 + 3x - 7 = 0$$

using an appropriate formula.

Give your answers correct to 1 decimal place. **4**

Marks

10. The diagram shows a mirror which has been designed for a new hotel.

The shape consists of a sector of a circle and a kite AOCB.

- The circle, centre O, has a radius of 50 centimetres.
- Angle AOC = 140 °.
- AB and CB are tangents to the circle at A and C respectively.

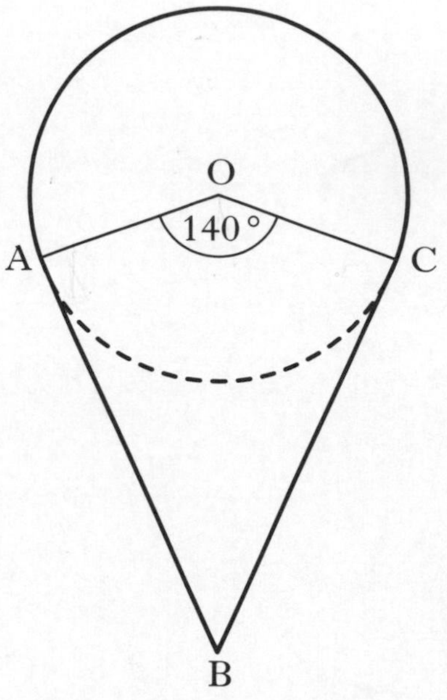

Find the perimeter of the mirror. **5**

11. (*a*) Solve the equation

$$4\tan x° + 5 = 0, \qquad 0 \leq x \leq 360.$$ **3**

(*b*) Show that

$$\tan x° \cos x° = \sin x°.$$ **2**

[*END OF QUESTION PAPER*]

[BLANK PAGE]

INTERMEDIATE 2 2002

X100/201

NATIONAL QUALIFICATIONS 2002

MONDAY, 27 MAY
1.00 PM – 1.45 PM

MATHEMATICS
INTERMEDIATE 2
Units 1, 2 and 3
Paper 1
(Non-calculator)

Read carefully

1 **You may NOT use a calculator.**

2 Full credit will be given only where the solution contains appropriate working.

3 Square-ruled paper is provided.

SCOTTISH QUALIFICATIONS AUTHORITY

LIB X100/201 6/21570

FORMULAE LIST

The roots of $ax^2 + bx + c = 0$ are $x = \dfrac{-b \pm \sqrt{(b^2 - 4ac)}}{2a}$

Sine rule: $\dfrac{a}{\sin A} = \dfrac{b}{\sin B} = \dfrac{c}{\sin C}$

Cosine rule: $a^2 = b^2 + c^2 - 2bc \cos A$ or $\cos A = \dfrac{b^2 + c^2 - a^2}{2bc}$

Area of a triangle: Area $= \frac{1}{2}ab \sin C$

Volume of a sphere: Volume $= \frac{4}{3}\pi r^3$

Volume of a cone: Volume $= \frac{1}{3}\pi r^2 h$

Volume of a cylinder: Volume $= \pi r^2 h$

Standard deviation: $s = \sqrt{\dfrac{\Sigma(x - \bar{x})^2}{n-1}} = \sqrt{\dfrac{\Sigma x^2 - (\Sigma x)^2/n}{n-1}}$, where n is the sample size.

ALL questions should be attempted.

Marks

1. In a tournament a group of golfers recorded the following scores.

74	70	71	73	75	71	73	72
72	75	71	76	74	72	70	73

(*a*) Construct a frequency table from the above data and add a cumulative frequency column. **2**

(*b*) What is the probability that a golfer chosen at random from this group recorded a score of less than 72? **1**

2.

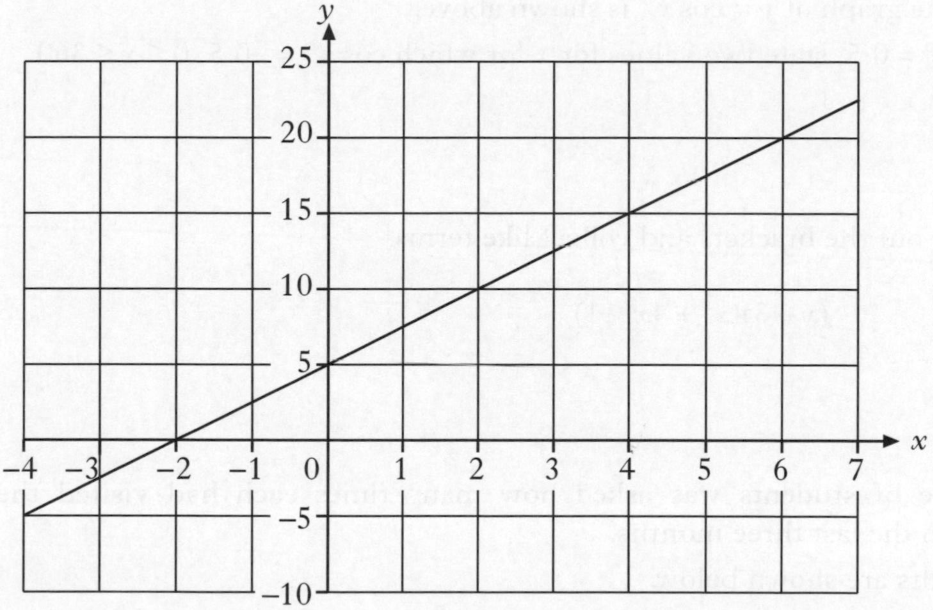

Find the equation of the straight line shown in the diagram. **3**

[Turn over

Marks

3.

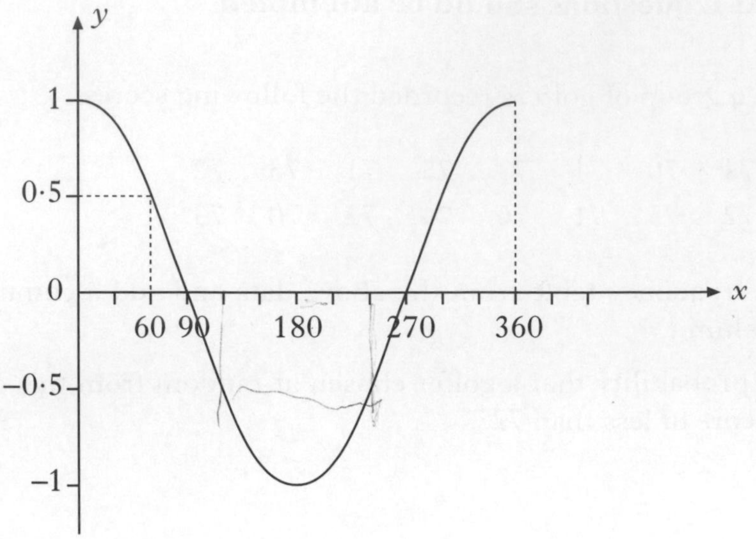

Part of the graph of $y = \cos x°$ is shown above.

If $\cos 60° = 0{\cdot}5$, state two values for x for which $\cos x° = -0{\cdot}5$, $0 \le x \le 360$. **2**

4. Multiply out the brackets and collect like terms.

$$(x - 3)(x^2 + 4x - 1)$$ **3**

5. A sample of students was asked how many times each had visited the cinema in the last three months.

The results are shown below.

4	5	4	1	4	3	2	2	4	6	2
3	4	4	1	3	1	2	3	1	1	

(*a*) From the above data, find the median, the lower quartile and the upper quartile. **3**

(*b*) Construct a boxplot for the data. **2**

(*c*) The same sample of students was asked how many times each had attended a football match in the same three months.

The boxplot below was drawn for this data.

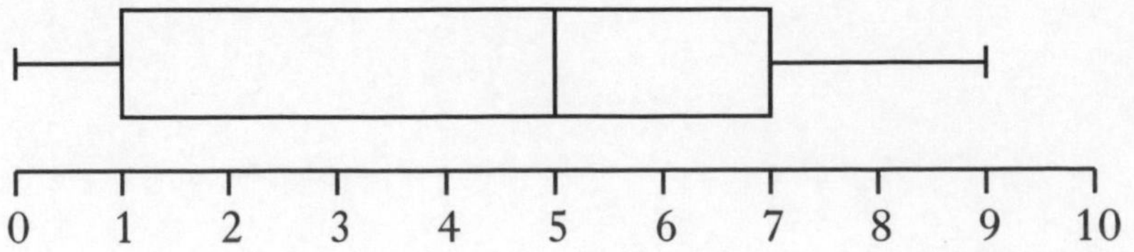

Compare the two boxplots and comment. **1**

Marks

6.

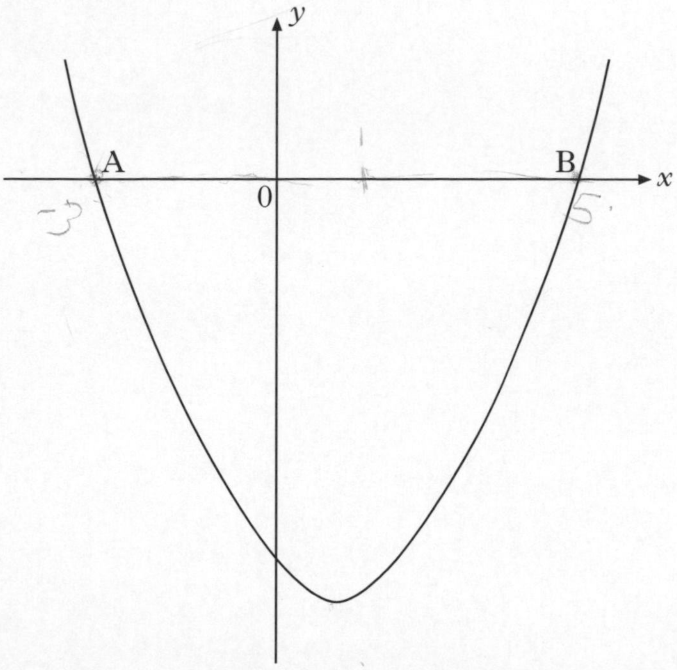

The equation of the parabola in the above diagram is

$$y = (x - 1)^2 - 16.$$

(*a*) State the coordinates of the minimum turning point of the parabola. **2**

(*b*) State the equation of the axis of symmetry of the parabola. **1**

(*c*) The parabola cuts the x-axis at A and B. Find the length of AB. **3**

7. (*a*) Express $\sqrt{45} - 2\sqrt{5}$ as a surd in its simplest form. **2**

(*b*) Express as a fraction in its simplest form

$$\frac{1}{x^2} + \frac{1}{x}, \qquad x \neq 0.$$ **2**

[*END OF QUESTION PAPER*]

[BLANK PAGE]

X100/203

NATIONAL QUALIFICATIONS 2002

MONDAY, 27 MAY
2.05 PM – 3.35 PM

MATHEMATICS
INTERMEDIATE 2
Units 1, 2 and 3
Paper 2

Read carefully

1 **Calculators may be used in this paper.**

2 Full credit will be given only where the solution contains appropriate working.

3 Square-ruled paper is provided.

SCOTTISH QUALIFICATIONS AUTHORITY

LIB X100/203 6/21570

FORMULAE LIST

The roots of $ax^2 + bx + c = 0$ are $x = \dfrac{-b \pm \sqrt{\left(b^2 - 4ac\right)}}{2a}$

Sine rule: $\dfrac{a}{\sin A} = \dfrac{b}{\sin B} = \dfrac{c}{\sin C}$

Cosine rule: $a^2 = b^2 + c^2 - 2bc \cos A$ or $\cos A = \dfrac{b^2 + c^2 - a^2}{2bc}$

Area of a triangle: Area $= \frac{1}{2}ab \sin C$

Volume of a sphere: Volume $= \frac{4}{3}\pi r^3$

Volume of a cone: Volume $= \frac{1}{3}\pi r^2 h$

Volume of a cylinder: Volume $= \pi r^2 h$

Standard deviation: $s = \sqrt{\dfrac{\Sigma(x - \bar{x})^2}{n-1}} = \sqrt{\dfrac{\Sigma x^2 - (\Sigma x)^2/n}{n-1}}$, where n is the sample size.

ALL questions should be attempted.

Marks

1. The sketch shows a triangle, ABC.

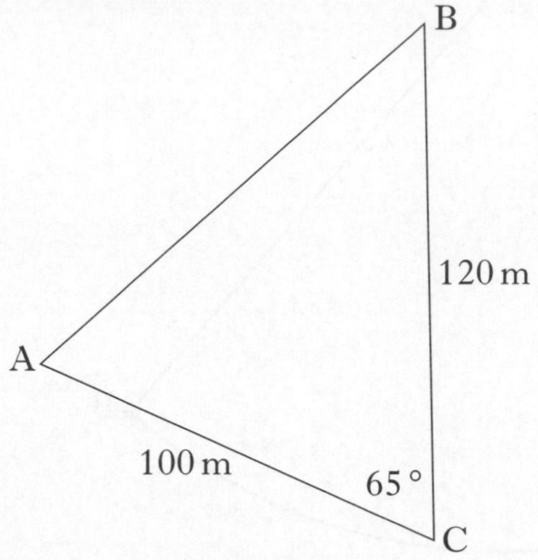

Calculate the area of the triangle. **2**

2. Solve **algebraically** the system of equations

$$3x - 2y = 11$$
$$2x + 5y = 1.$$ **3**

3. (*a*) The price, in pence, of a carton of milk in six different supermarkets is shown below.

66 70 89 75 79 59

Use an appropriate formula to calculate the mean and standard deviation of these prices.
Show clearly all your working. **4**

(*b*) In six local shops, the mean price of a carton of milk is 73 pence with a standard deviation of 17·7.
Compare the supermarket prices with those of the local shops. **2**

[Turn over

Marks

4. A pendulum travels along an arc of a circle, centre C.

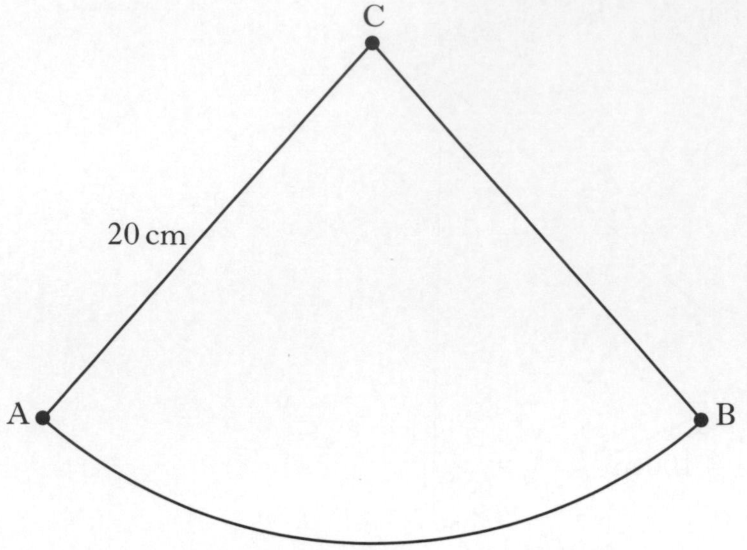

The length of the pendulum is 20 centimetres.

The pendulum swings from A to B.

The length of the arc AB is 28·6 centimetres.

Find the angle through which the pendulum swings from A to B. **4**

5. (*a*) (i) Factorise completely

$$3y^2 - 6y.$$ **1**

(ii) Factorise

$$y^2 + y - 6.$$ **2**

(*b*) Hence express $\dfrac{3y^2 - 6y}{y^2 + y - 6}$ in its simplest form. **2**

Marks

6. A container to hold chocolates is in the shape of part of a cone with dimensions as shown below.

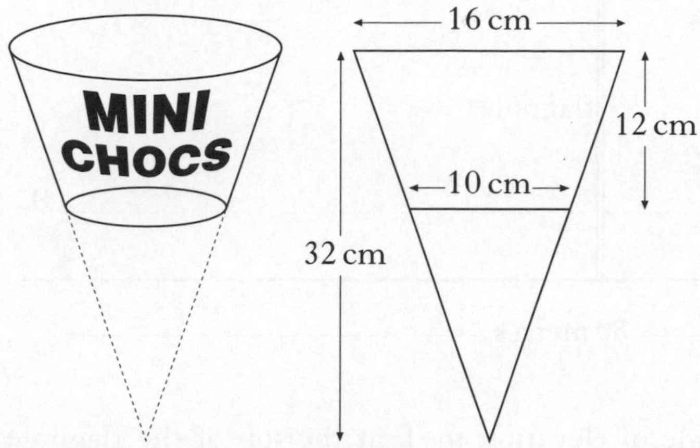

Calculate the volume of the container.

Give your answer correct to one significant figure. **5**

7. Solve the equation

$$2x^2 + 3x - 1 = 0,$$

giving your answers correct to one decimal place. **4**

[Turn over

Marks

8. The diagram shows two positions of a surveyor as he views the top of a flagpole.

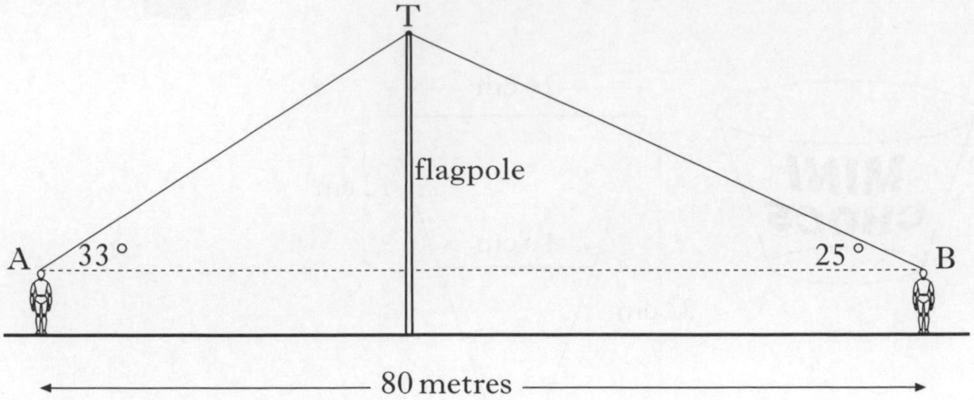

From position A, the angle of elevation to T at the top of the flagpole is 33°.

From position B, the angle of elevation to T at the top of the flagpole is 25°.

The distance AB is 80 metres and the height of the surveyor to eye level is 1·6 metres.

Find the height of the flagpole. **6**

Marks

9. The diagram below shows a circular cross-section of a cylindrical oil tank.

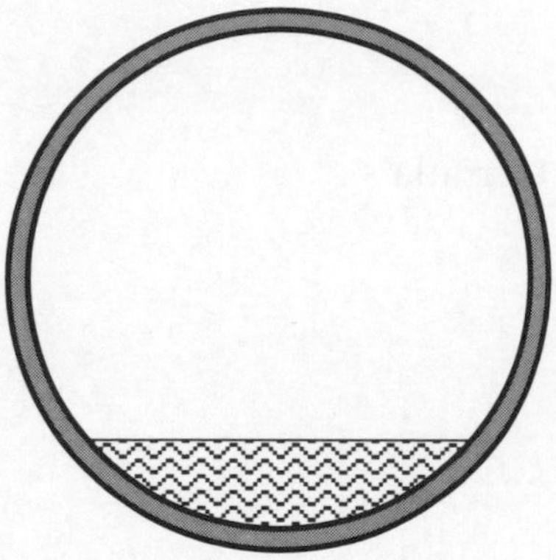

In the figure below,

- O represents the centre of the circle
- PQ represents the surface of the oil in the tank
- PQ is 3 metres
- the radius OP is 2·5 metres.

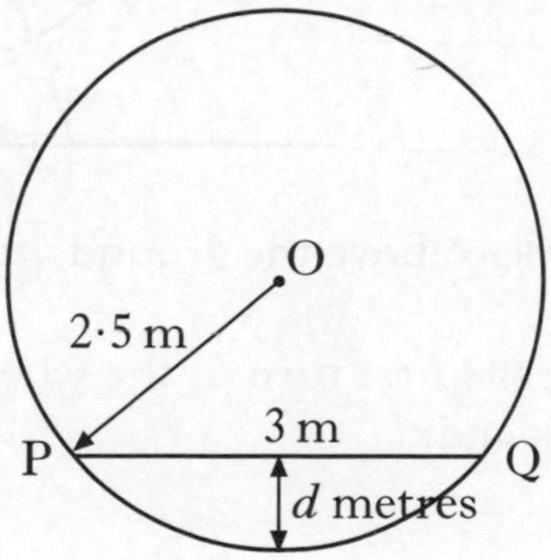

Find the depth, d metres, of oil in the tank. **4**

10. The population of Newtown is 50 000.

The population of Newtown is **increasing** at a steady rate of 5% per annum.

The population of Coaltown is 108 000.

The population of Coaltown is **decreasing** at a steady rate of 20% per annum.

How many years will it take until the population of Newtown is greater than the population of Coaltown? **5**

[Turn over for Questions 11 and 12 on *Page eight*

Marks

11. (*a*) Simplify

$$6x^{\frac{3}{2}} \div 2x^{\frac{1}{2}}.$$ **2**

(*b*) Change the subject of the formula

$$r = 3p + 2t$$

to p. **2**

12. At the carnival, the height, H metres, of a carriage on the big wheel above the ground is given by the formula

$$H = 10 + 5\sin t°,$$

t seconds after starting to turn.

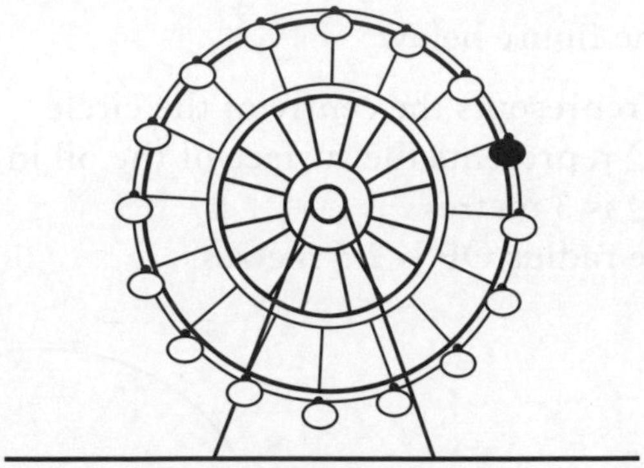

(*a*) Find the height of the carriage above the ground after 10 seconds. **2**

(*b*) Find the **two** times during the first turn of the wheel when the carriage is 12·5 metres above the ground. **4**

[*END OF QUESTION PAPER*]

INTERMEDIATE 2 2002
WINTER DIET

W100/201

NATIONAL
QUALIFICATIONS
2002

FRIDAY, 18 JANUARY
9.00 AM – 9.45 AM

MATHEMATICS
INTERMEDIATE 2
Units 1, 2 and 3
Paper 1
(Non-calculator)

Read carefully

1 **You may <u>NOT</u> use a calculator.**

2 Full credit will be given only where the solution contains appropriate working.

3 Square-ruled paper is provided.

SCOTTISH
QUALIFICATIONS
AUTHORITY

FORMULAE LIST

The roots of $ax^2 + bx + c = 0$ are $x = \dfrac{-b \pm \sqrt{(b^2 - 4ac)}}{2a}$

Sine rule: $\dfrac{a}{\sin A} = \dfrac{b}{\sin B} = \dfrac{c}{\sin C}$

Cosine rule: $a^2 = b^2 + c^2 - 2bc \cos A$ or $\cos A = \dfrac{b^2 + c^2 - a^2}{2bc}$

Area of a triangle: Area $= \frac{1}{2}ab \sin C$

Volume of a sphere: Volume $= \frac{4}{3}\pi r^3$

Volume of a cone: Volume $= \frac{1}{3}\pi r^2 h$

Volume of a cylinder: Volume $= \pi r^2 h$

Standard deviation: $s = \sqrt{\dfrac{\Sigma(x - \bar{x})^2}{n-1}} = \sqrt{\dfrac{\Sigma x^2 - (\Sigma x)^2 / n}{n-1}}$, where n is the sample size.

ALL questions should be attempted.

Marks

1. The marks of a group of students in a class test and in the final exam are shown in the scattergraph below.

A line of best fit has been drawn.

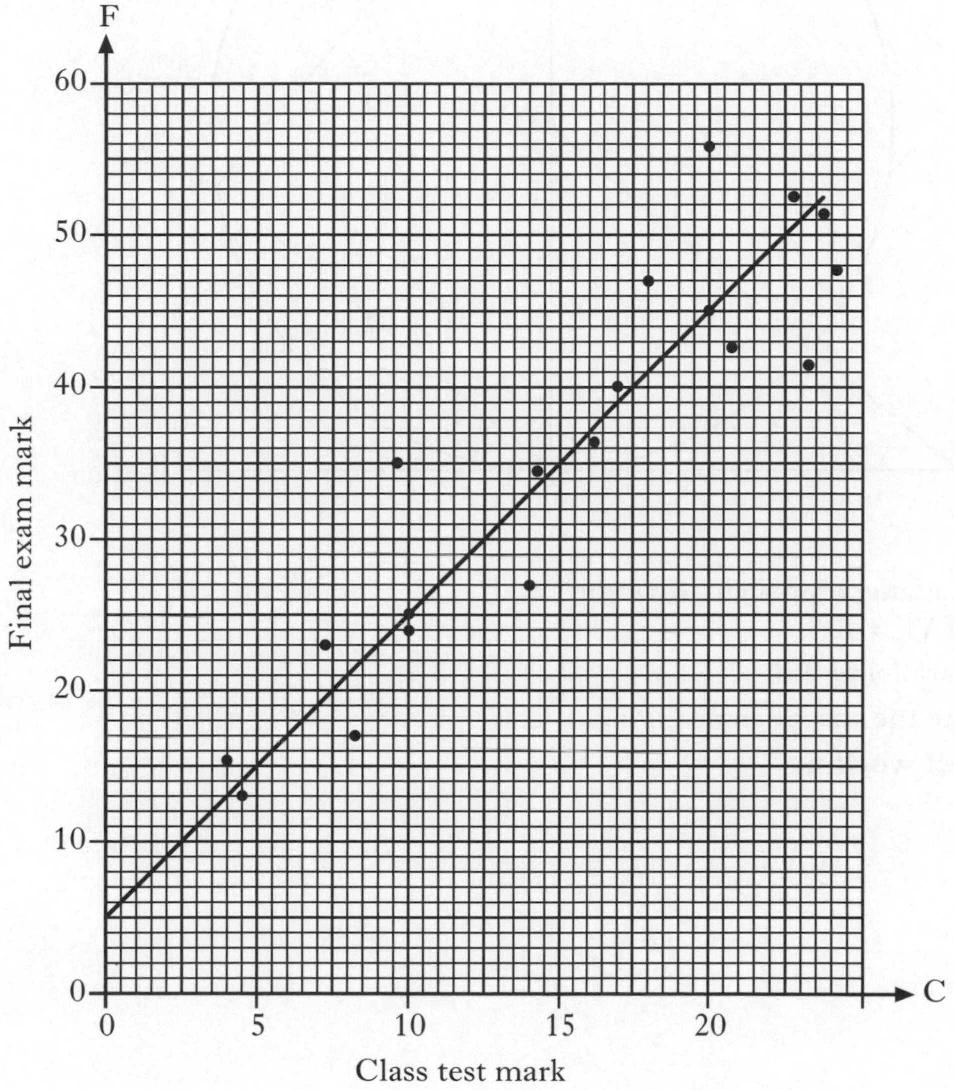

(*a*) Find the equation of the line of best fit. **3**

(*b*) **Use your answer to part (*a*)** to predict the final exam mark for a student who achieved a mark of 12 in the class test. **1**

[Turn over

Marks

2.

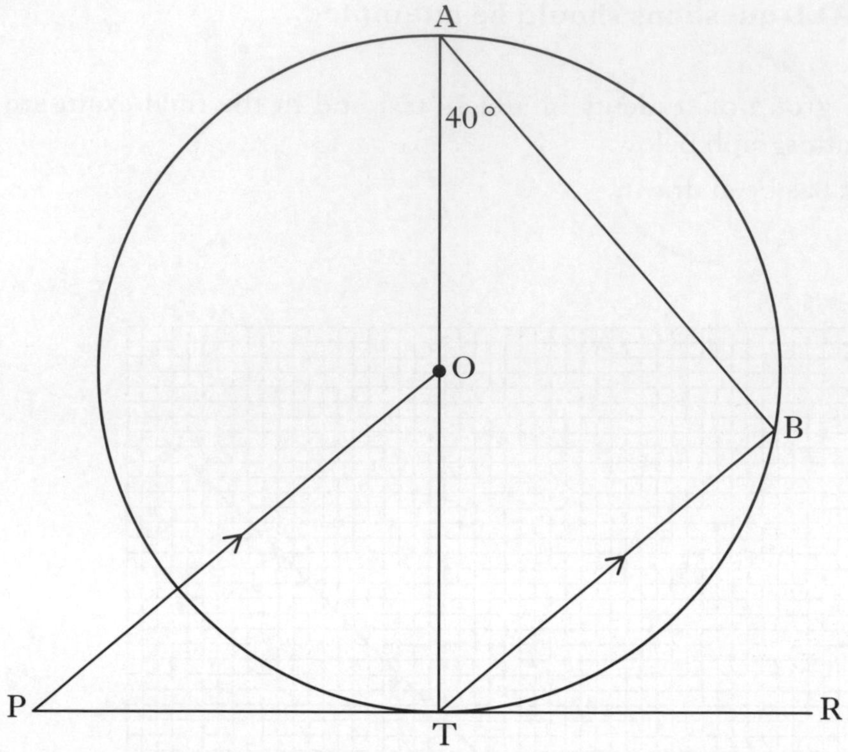

PTR is a tangent to a circle, centre O.

Angle BAT = 40°.

PO is parallel to TB.

Calculate the size of angle OPT.

Show all working. 3

Marks

3. The stem and leaf diagram shows the heights, to the nearest centimetre, of a group of female students.

14	8					
15	6					
16	0	4	8	9		
17	1	2	4	4	5	8
18	8					

$n = 13$ 14|8 represents 148 cm

(*a*) Using the above information, find

(i) the median **1**

(ii) the lower quartile and the upper quartile. **2**

(*b*) Draw a boxplot to illustrate this data. **2**

(*c*) A sample of male students from the same course was taken. The heights, to the nearest centimetre, of these students were recorded.

The boxplot, shown below, illustrates this new data.

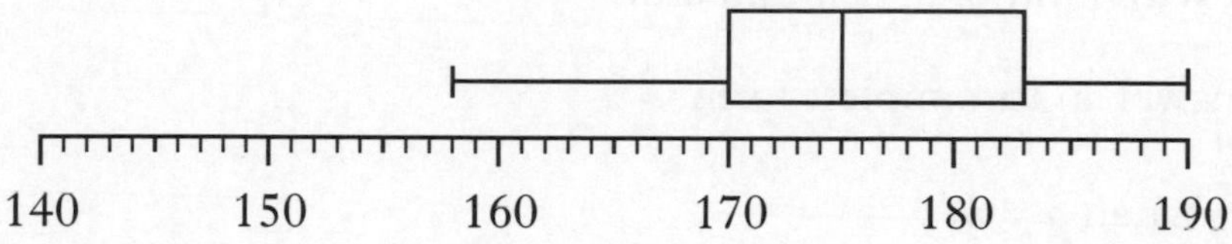

By comparing the boxplots, make **two** appropriate comments about the heights of the female and the male students. **2**

[Turn over

Marks

4. The diagram below shows the graph of $y = ax^2$.

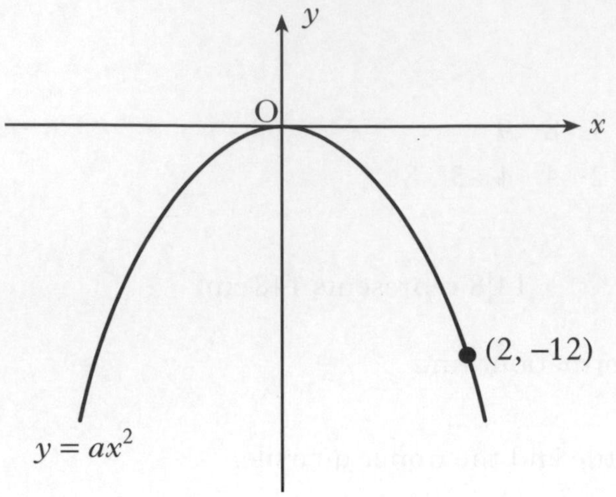

Find the value of a. **2**

5. (*a*) Express $\frac{10}{\sqrt{5}}$ with a rational denominator.

Give your answer in its simplest form. **2**

(*b*) Evaluate $4a^{\frac{2}{3}}$ when $a = 27$. **2**

6. The graph shown below has an equation of the form $y = \cos(x - b)°$.

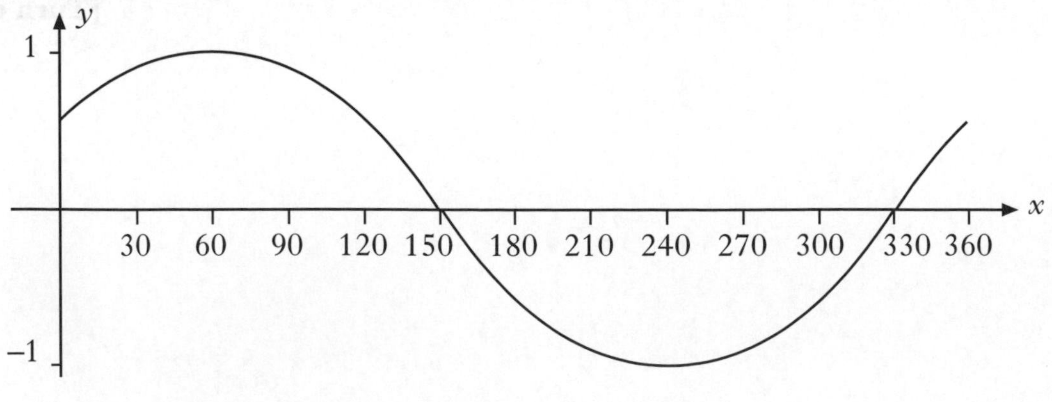

Write down the value of b. **1**

Marks

7.

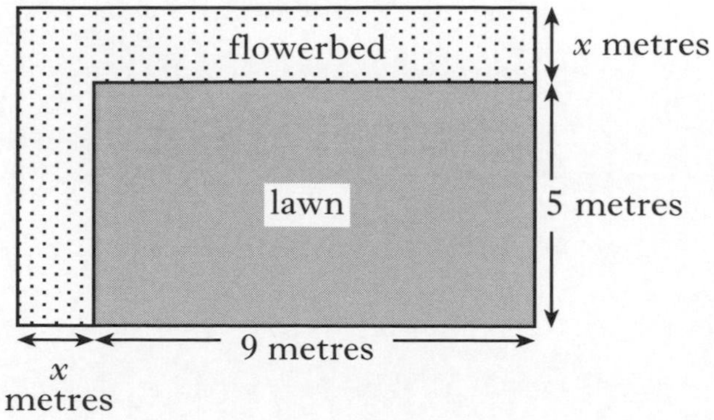

The diagram shows a rectangular garden which consists of a rectangular lawn and a flowerbed along two sides of the lawn

- the lawn measures 9 metres by 5 metres
- the width of the flowerbed is x metres.

(*a*) State the length and breadth of the garden. **1**

(*b*) Show that the area, A square metres, of the garden is given by

$$A = x^2 + 14x + 45.$$ **2**

(*c*) The area of the garden is 77 square metres. Find the width of the flowerbed.

Show clearly all your working. **3**

[*END OF QUESTION PAPER*]

[BLANK PAGE]

W100/203

NATIONAL QUALIFICATIONS 2002

FRIDAY, 18 JANUARY
10.05 AM – 11.35 AM

MATHEMATICS
INTERMEDIATE 2
Units 1, 2 and 3
Paper 2

Read carefully

1 **Calculators may be used in this paper.**

2 Full credit will be given only where the solution contains appropriate working.

3 Square-ruled paper is provided.

LIB W100/203 6/920

FORMULAE LIST

The roots of $ax^2 + bx + c = 0$ are $x = \dfrac{-b \pm \sqrt{(b^2 - 4ac)}}{2a}$

Sine rule: $\dfrac{a}{\sin A} = \dfrac{b}{\sin B} = \dfrac{c}{\sin C}$

Cosine rule: $a^2 = b^2 + c^2 - 2bc \cos A$ or $\cos A = \dfrac{b^2 + c^2 - a^2}{2bc}$

Area of a triangle: Area $= \frac{1}{2}ab \sin C$

Volume of a sphere: Volume $= \frac{4}{3}\pi r^3$

Volume of a cone: Volume $= \frac{1}{3}\pi r^2 h$

Volume of a cylinder: Volume $= \pi r^2 h$

Standard deviation: $s = \sqrt{\dfrac{\Sigma(x - \bar{x})^2}{n-1}} = \sqrt{\dfrac{\Sigma x^2 - (\Sigma x)^2/n}{n-1}}$, where n is the sample size.

ALL questions should be attempted.

Marks

1. Change the subject of the formula

$$x = y^2 - m$$

to y. **2**

2. In the diagram opposite AC and BD are arcs of circles with centres at O.

The radius, OA, is 8 metres and the radius, OB, is 10 metres.

Angle AOC = 72°.

Find the shaded area. **4**

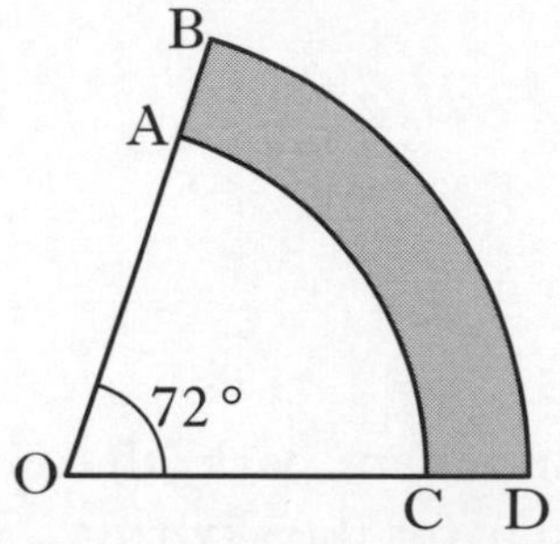

3. The value of a house increased from £85 000 to £86 700 in one year.

(*a*) What was the percentage increase? **1**

(*b*) If the value of the house continued to rise at this rate, what would its value be after a **further** 3 years?
Give your answer to the nearest thousand pounds. **3**

[Turn over

Marks

4. A grain store is in the shape of a cylinder with a hemisphere on top as shown in the diagram.

The cylinder has radius 2·4 metres and height 9·5 metres.

Find the volume of the grain store.

Give your answer in cubic metres, correct to 1 significant figure. **4**

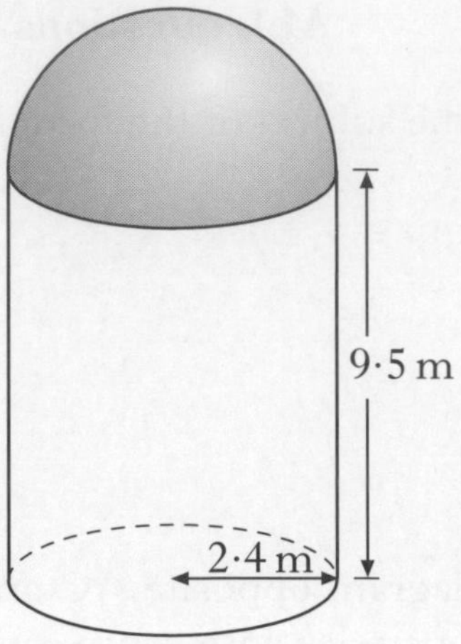

5. At an amusement park, the Green family buy 3 tickets for the ghost train and 2 tickets for the sky ride. The total cost is £8·60.

(*a*) Let x pounds be the cost of a ticket for the ghost train and y pounds be the cost of a ticket for the sky ride.

Write down an equation in x and y which satisfies the above condition. **1**

(*b*) The Black family bought 5 tickets for the ghost train and 3 tickets for the sky ride at the same amusement park. The total cost was £13·60.

Write down a second equation in x and y which satisfies this condition. **1**

(*c*) Find the cost of a ticket for the ghost train and the cost of a ticket for the sky ride. **4**

Marks

6. Harry records the amount, in pounds, he earned from his part-time job each week for ten weeks.

14 18 19 20 17 19 18 20 15 22

He calculates that

$$\sum x = 182 \qquad \text{and} \qquad \sum x^2 = 3364$$

where x is the amount in pounds he earned each week.

(*a*) Calculate the mean amount he earned per week. **1**

(*b*) Using an appropriate formula, calculate the standard deviation. **2**

(*c*) Irene and Harry compare their earnings over the ten week period. For each of the ten weeks, Irene earns exactly £5 more than Harry.

State:

(i) the mean amount Irene earned per week; **1**

(ii) the standard deviation of Irene's earnings. **1**

7. A field with sides measuring 12·5 metres, 13·2 metres and 10·7 metres is represented by the triangle PQR shown below.

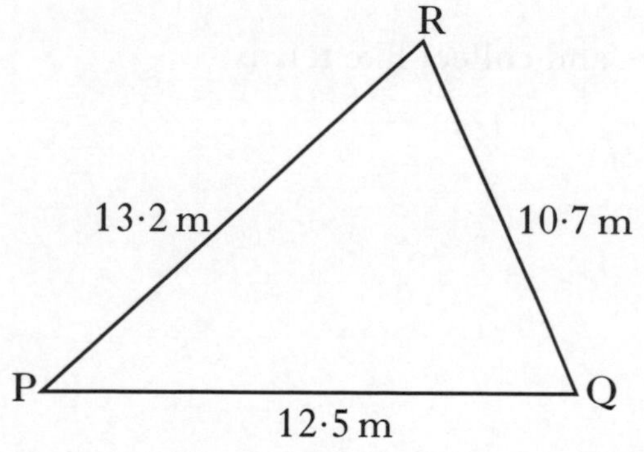

(*a*) Calculate the size of angle PQR.

Do not use a scale drawing. **3**

(*b*) Calculate the area of the field. **2**

[Turn over

Marks

8. Solve the equation

$$2p^2 - 3p - 1 = 0,$$

giving the roots correct to 1 decimal place. **4**

9. To calculate the height of a cliff, a surveyor measures the angle of elevation at two positions A and B as shown in the diagram below.

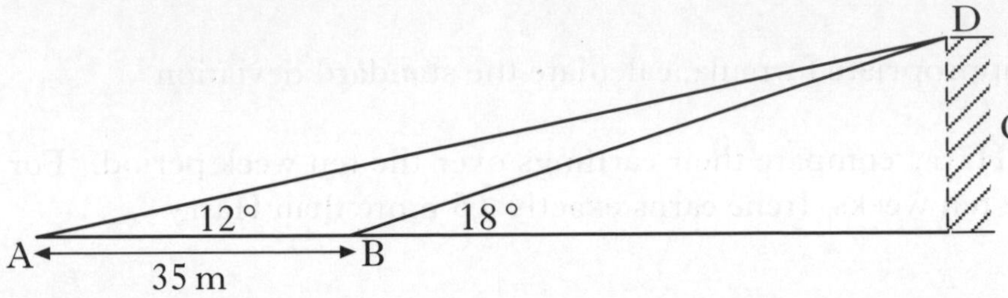

At A, the angle of elevation to D, the top of the cliff, is 12 °.

At B, the angle of elevation to D is 18 °.

AB is 35 metres.

Calculate the height of the cliff. **5**

10. (*a*) Multiply out the brackets and collect like terms.

$$(2x + 3)(x^2 - 5x + 2)$$ **3**

(*b*) Factorise

$$2x^2 - 7x - 9.$$ **2**

11. Solve the equation

$$2\tan x° + 4 = 5, \quad 0 \leq x < 360.$$ **3**

Marks

12. (*a*) Simplify

$$\frac{b^{\frac{5}{2}} \times b^{-\frac{1}{2}}}{b}.$$ **2**

(*b*) Express $\frac{4}{x} - \frac{3}{x-3}$, $x \neq 0,\ x \neq 3$, as a single fraction in its simplest form. **3**

(*c*) Prove that

$$(\cos x° + \sin x°)^2 = 1 + 2\sin x° \cos x°.$$ **2**

[*END OF QUESTION PAPER*]

[BLANK PAGE]

INTERMEDIATE 2 2003

X100/201

NATIONAL
QUALIFICATIONS
2003

WEDNESDAY, 21 MAY
1.30 PM – 2.15 PM

MATHEMATICS
INTERMEDIATE 2
Units 1, 2 and 3
Paper 1
(Non-calculator)

Read carefully

1 **You may NOT use a calculator.**

2 Full credit will be given only where the solution contains appropriate working.

3 Square-ruled paper is provided.

SCOTTISH
QUALIFICATIONS
AUTHORITY

FORMULAE LIST

The roots of $ax^2 + bx + c = 0$ are $x = \dfrac{-b \pm \sqrt{(b^2 - 4ac)}}{2a}$

Sine rule: $\dfrac{a}{\sin A} = \dfrac{b}{\sin B} = \dfrac{c}{\sin C}$

Cosine rule: $a^2 = b^2 + c^2 - 2bc \cos A$ or $\cos A = \dfrac{b^2 + c^2 - a^2}{2bc}$

Area of a triangle: Area $= \frac{1}{2}ab \sin C$

Volume of a sphere: Volume $= \frac{4}{3}\pi r^3$

Volume of a cone: Volume $= \frac{1}{3}\pi r^2 h$

Volume of a cylinder: Volume $= \pi r^2 h$

Standard deviation: $s = \sqrt{\dfrac{\sum(x - \bar{x})^2}{n-1}} = \sqrt{\dfrac{\sum x^2 - (\sum x)^2 / n}{n-1}}$, where n is the sample size.

ALL questions should be attempted.

Marks

1. Multiply out the brackets and collect like terms.

$(2a - b)(3a + 2b)$ **2**

2. Two spinners are used in an experiment.

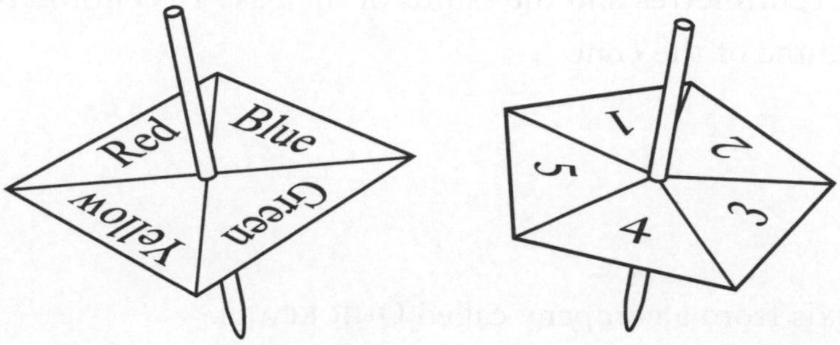

The table below shows some of the possible outcomes when both spinners are spun and allowed to come to rest.

	1	2	3	4	5
Red	R,1	R,2			
Yellow	Y,1				
Blue	B,1				
Green	G,1				

(*a*) Copy and complete the table. **1**

(*b*) What is the probability that one spinner comes to rest on red and the other on an even number? **1**

[Turn over

Marks

3. The diagram shows a cone.

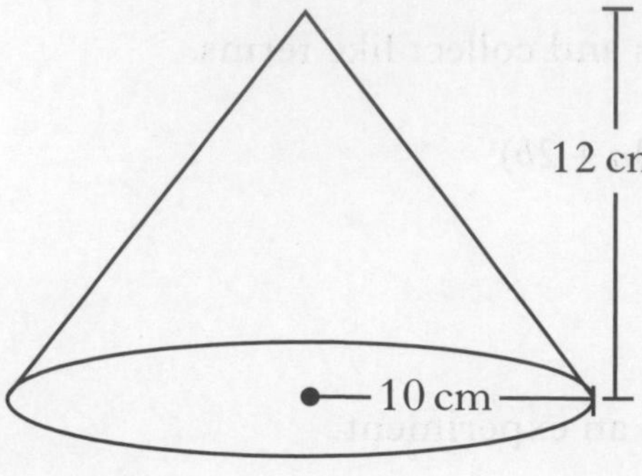

The height is 12 centimetres and the radius of the base 10 centimetres.

Calculate the volume of the cone.

Take $\pi = 3{\cdot}14$. 2

4. A hotel books taxis from a company called QUICKCARS.

The receptionist notes the waiting time for every taxi ordered over a period of two weeks.

The times are recorded in the stem and leaf diagram shown below.

Waiting time (minutes)

0	6 7
1	2 3 4
2	5 6 9 9
3	2 5 7
4	2 4

$n = 14$ 1 | 3 represents 13 minutes

(*a*) For the given data, calculate:

(i) the median; 1

(ii) the lower quartile; 1

(iii) the upper quartile. 1

(*b*) Calculate the semi-interquartile range. 1

In another two week period, the hotel books taxis from a company called FASTCABS.

The semi-interquartile range for FASTCABS is found to be 2·5 minutes.

(*c*) Which company provides the more consistent service?

Give a reason for your answer. 1

Marks

7.

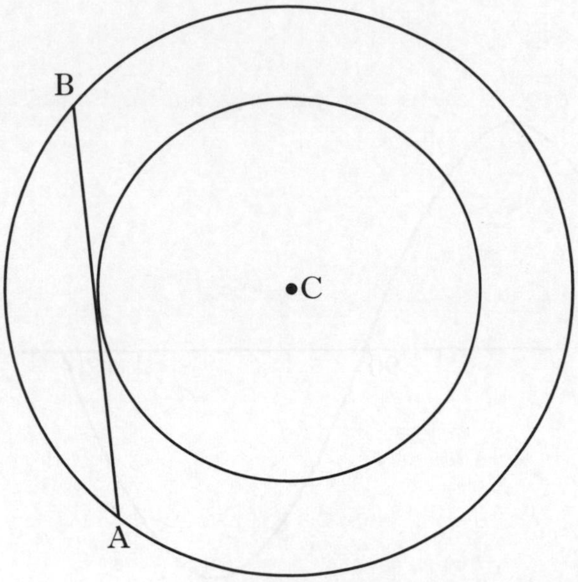

C is the centre of two concentric circles.

AB is a tangent to the smaller circle and a chord of the larger circle.

The radius of the smaller circle is 6 centimetres and the chord AB has length 16 centimetres.

Calculate the radius of the larger circle. **3**

8. (*a*) Factorise $7 + 6x - x^2$. **2**

(*b*) Hence write down the roots of the equation

$$7 + 6x - x^2 = 0.$$ **1**

(*c*) The graph of $y = 7 + 6x - x^2$ is shown in the diagram.

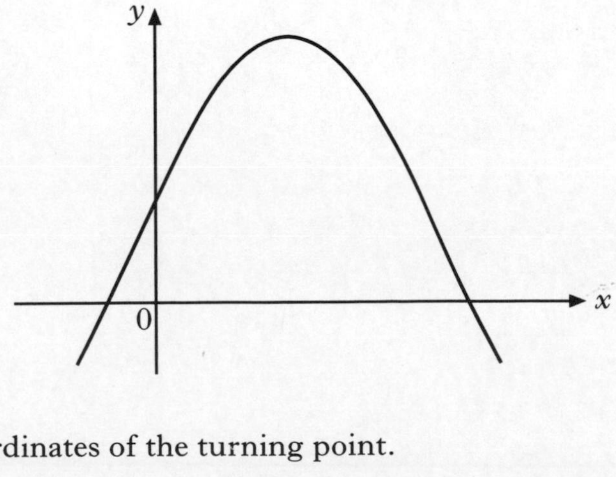

Find the coordinates of the turning point. **3**

[*END OF QUESTION PAPER*]

Marks

5. Part of the graph of $y = a\sin bx°$ is shown in the diagram.

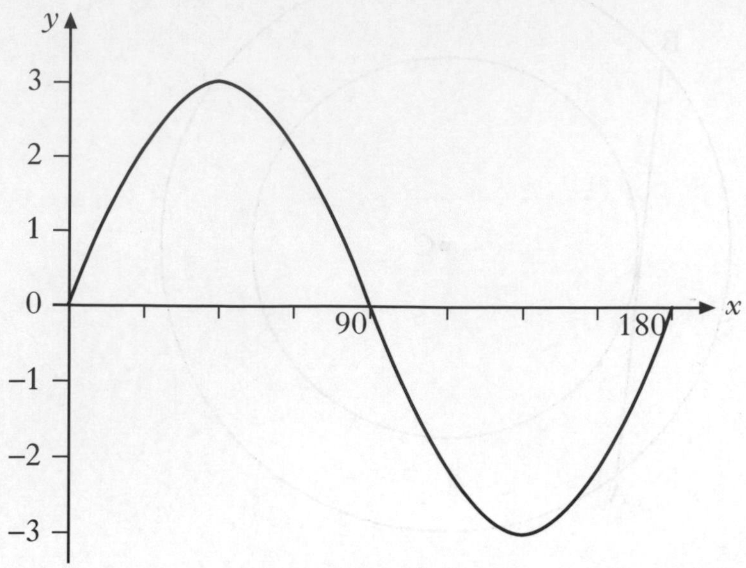

State the values of a and b. **2**

6. (*a*) Express $\dfrac{\sqrt{40}}{\sqrt{2}}$ as a surd in its simplest form. **2**

(*b*) Simplify $\dfrac{2x+2}{(x+1)^2}$. **2**

[Turn over for Questions 7 and 8 on *Page six*

X100/203

NATIONAL QUALIFICATIONS 2003

WEDNESDAY, 21 MAY
2.35 PM – 4.05 PM

MATHEMATICS
INTERMEDIATE 2
Units 1, 2 and 3
Paper 2

Read carefully

1 **Calculators may be used in this paper.**

2 Full credit will be given only where the solution contains appropriate working.

3 Square-ruled paper is provided.

LIB X100/203 6/3/22570

FORMULAE LIST

The roots of $ax^2 + bx + c = 0$ are $x = \frac{-b \pm \sqrt{(b^2 - 4ac)}}{2a}$

Sine rule: $\frac{a}{\sin A} = \frac{b}{\sin B} = \frac{c}{\sin C}$

Cosine rule: $a^2 = b^2 + c^2 - 2bc \cos A$ or $\cos A = \frac{b^2 + c^2 - a^2}{2bc}$

Area of a triangle: Area $= \frac{1}{2}ab \sin C$

Volume of a sphere: Volume $= \frac{4}{3}\pi r^3$

Volume of a cone: Volume $= \frac{1}{3}\pi r^2 h$

Volume of a cylinder: Volume $= \pi r^2 h$

Standard deviation: $s = \sqrt{\frac{\sum(x - \bar{x})^2}{n-1}} = \sqrt{\frac{\sum x^2 - (\sum x)^2 / n}{n-1}}$, where n is the sample size.

ALL questions should be attempted.

Marks

1.

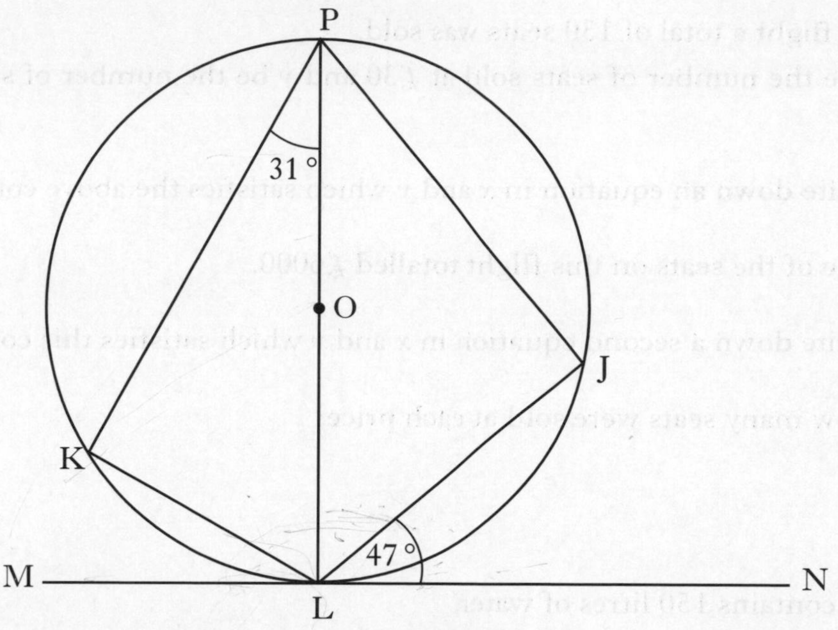

The tangent, MN, touches the circle, centre O, at L.

Angle JLN = 47 °.

Angle KPL = 31 °.

Find the size of angle KLJ. **3**

2. A sample of shoppers was asked which brand of washing powder they preferred.

The responses are shown below.

Washing Powder	*Frequency*
Dazzle	250
Cyclo	375
Surfer	125
Cleano	250

Construct a pie chart to illustrate this information.

Show all your working. **3**

[Turn over

Marks

3. Seats on flights from London to Edinburgh are sold at two prices, £30 and £50.

On one flight a total of 130 seats was sold.

Let x be the number of seats sold at £30 and y be the number of seats sold at £50.

(*a*) Write down an equation in x and y which satisfies the above condition. **1**

The sale of the seats on this flight totalled £6000.

(*b*) Write down a second equation in x and y which satisfies this condition. **1**

(*c*) How many seats were sold at each price? **4**

4. A bath contains 150 litres of water.

Water is drained from the bath at a steady rate of 30 litres per minute.

The graph of the volume, V litres, of water in the bath against the time, t minutes, is shown below.

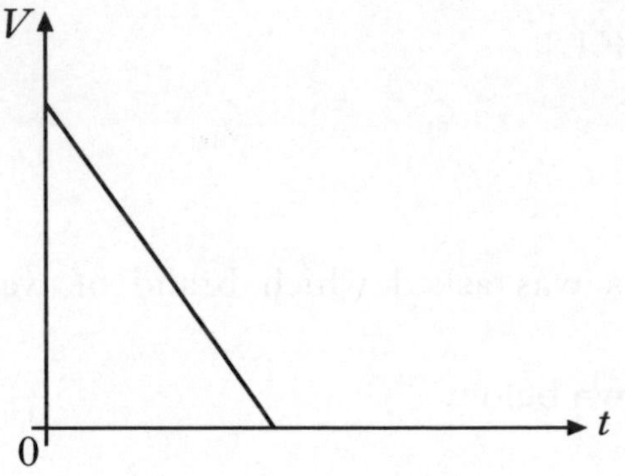

Write down an equation connecting V and t. **3**

Marks

5. A gardener grows tomatoes in his greenhouse.

The temperature of the greenhouse, in degrees Celsius, is recorded every day at noon for one week.

17 22 25 16 21 16 16

(*a*) For the given temperatures, calculate:

(i) the mean; **1**

(ii) the standard deviation. **3**

Show clearly all your working.

For best growth, the mean temperature should be (20 ± 5)°C and the standard deviation should be less than 5 °C.

(*b*) Are the conditions in the greenhouse likely to result in best growth?

Explain clearly your answer. **2**

[Turn over

Marks

6. A garden trough is in the shape of a prism.

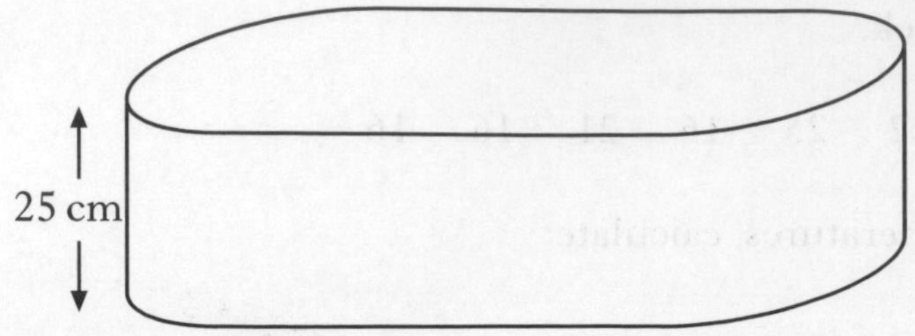

The height of the trough is 25 centimetres.

The cross-section of the trough consists of a rectangle and two semi-circles with measurements as shown.

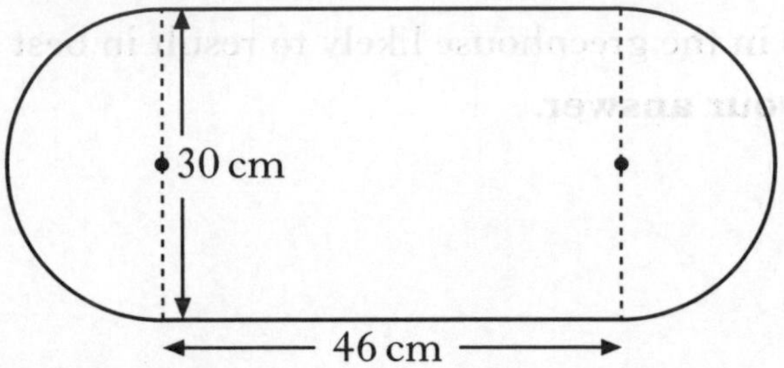

(*a*) Find the volume of the garden trough in cubic centimetres.
Give your answer correct to two significant figures. **4**

A new design of garden trough is planned by the manufacturer.

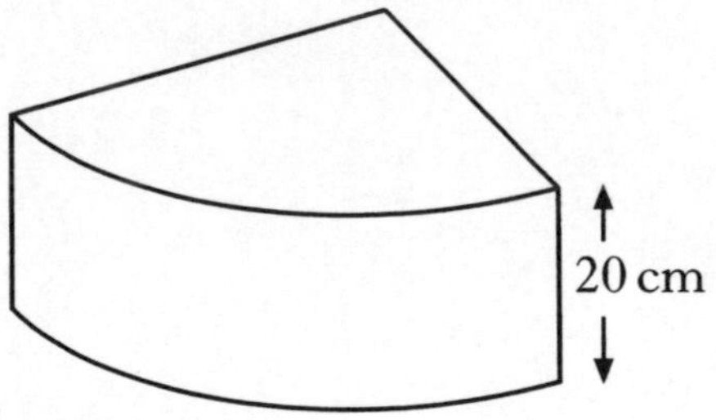

The height of the trough is 20 cm.

The uniform cross-section of this trough is a quarter of a circle.

The volume of the trough is 30 000 cm^3.

(*b*) Find the radius of the cross-section. **3**

Marks

7. Change the subject of the formula

$$y = ax^2 + c \qquad \text{to } x.$$ 3

8. The diagram below shows a big wheel at a fairground.

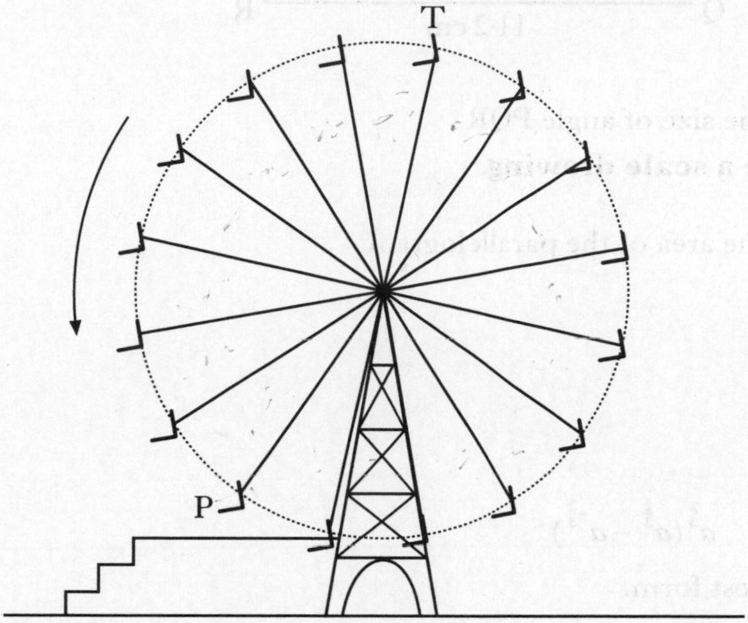

The wheel has sixteen chairs equally spaced on its circumference.
The radius of the wheel is 9 metres.
As the wheel rotates in an anticlockwise direction, find the distance a chair travels in moving from position T to position P in the diagram. 4

9. Solve the equation

$$2x^2 + 4x - 9 = 0,$$

giving the roots correct to one decimal place. 4

[Turn over for Questions 10 to 12 on *Page eight*

Marks

10. The sketch shows a parallelogram, PQRS.

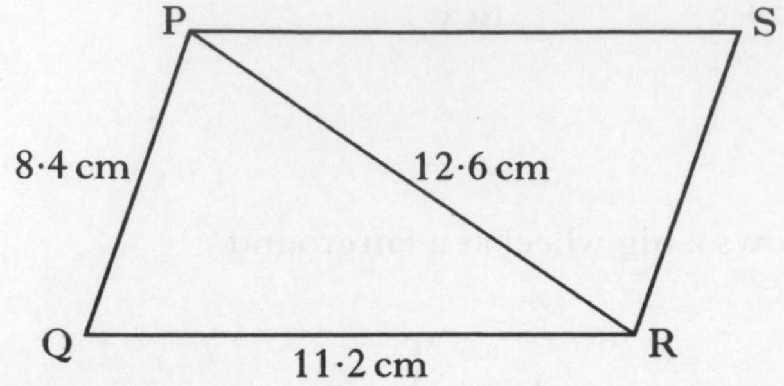

(*a*) Calculate the size of angle PQR.
Do not use a scale drawing. **3**

(*b*) Calculate the area of the parallelogram. **3**

11. (*a*) Express

$$a^{\frac{2}{3}}(a^{\frac{2}{3}} - a^{-\frac{2}{3}})$$

in its simplest form. **2**

(*b*) Express

$$\frac{a}{x} - \frac{b}{y}, \qquad x \neq 0, \ y \neq 0,$$

as a fraction in its simplest form. **2**

12. (*a*) Solve the equation

$$2\tan x° + 7 = 0, \qquad 0 \leq x < 360.$$ **3**

(*b*) Prove that

$$\sin^3 x° + \sin x° \cos^2 x° = \sin x°.$$ **2**

[*END OF QUESTION PAPER*]